"I have been kissed before, you know!"

Ford just looked at her, raised one eyebrow and then laughed! Then his mouth swooped down to capture her own....

As abruptly as it had begun, the embrace was ended. "You affect me in the most amazing ways, Saunders."

"I...I wish you wouldn't talk like that," she replied.

"Why not? Don't you want to know how I feel? Or is it your own feelings you're so afraid of?"

Victoria Gordon is a former journalist who began writing romances in 1979. Canadian-born, she moved to Australia in the early seventies and settled in northern Tasmania before returning to her native Canada. She has judged retrieving trials for gundogs and is active in a variety of other outdoor activities when not chained to her magic word-processing machine.

An Irresistible Flirtation
Victoria Gordon

Harlequin Books

TORONTO • NEW YORK • LONDON
AMSTERDAM • PARIS • SYDNEY • HAMBURG
STOCKHOLM • ATHENS • TOKYO • MILAN
MADRID • WARSAW • BUDAPEST • AUCKLAND

ISBN 0-373-17318-0

AN IRRESISTIBLE FLIRTATION

First North American Publication 1997.

Printed in U.S.A.

CHAPTER ONE

SAUNDERS stood in shocked, silent disbelief, the strident tones of Charlotte's diatribe ringing in her ears. She wanted to be somewhere—anywhere—else, did *not* want to be a party to this blistering feminist attack, didn't believe in it, didn't like it, didn't want any part of it.

But mostly she wanted to be able at least to look away, avert her gaze and look at the floor, or the splendid cast-brass sculpture that overhung the entrance to the building, or the people emerging from the lifts. At anything, she thought, but the angry man who stood there, shrugging Charlotte's verbal assault from unbelievably broad shoulders and glaring at Saunders with black, accusing eyes.

At me! why are you glaring at me?

She wanted to scream out her innocence, to tell him that it wasn't *she* who had taken offence at his perfectly innocent, mannerly gesture of holding the door open for she and Charlotte to pass through. It wasn't *she* who had launched into this most astonishing verbal tirade on the subject of male chauvinist pigs and dominance and. . . Insanity, she thought.

Glare at Charlotte, why don't you? *She's* the feminist! I haven't said a word. I wouldn't. I couldn't!

The man had the broadest shoulders and the darkest eyes she had ever seen. Truly black eyes, eyes like pools of ink, as dark as his hair must once have been, before the patina of silver had begun to dominate its

5

sleek, harsh straightness. Eyes that seemed to sear into her own—accusing, contemptuous, sneering. Eyes that now, apparently bored with her lack of response, abandoned her own eyes to roam down the planes of her face, lingering at her throat, lingering longer at where her breasts pushed at the fabric of her silk blouse. Eyes that then sauntered boldly to touch at her hips, to follow the line of her dark skirt until she could almost see them actually *measuring* the exact one-inch-below-the-knee length of the skirt.

He ignored her legs, or seemed to. Not surprising, she found herself thinking. They were fine as legs went, but too skinny, like the rest of her. And then she had to choke back the chuckle that rose to her lips just at the idea of thinking such a thing at a time like this.

Because he was glaring into her eyes again, and she found herself feeling once more that his own were live coals, smouldering beneath the thick ebony eyebrows—just waiting to leap out somehow and incinerate her.

Not me! The words came silently to her mind, but for some reason refused to reach her lips. *His* lips had shifted slightly, one edge of his mouth curling into what could have been either a sneer or a knowing half-smile of satisfaction.

One strong, tanned, long-fingered hand was still holding open the door. People were moving to and fro through the door, most of them casting startled glances at the tableau, but not daring, Saunders thought, to stop and actually listen to Charlotte's attack. One look at those smouldering eyes would be enough to put off even the bravest who might think to intervene.

'So there!'

And Charlotte turned, her tall, slender figure rigid with her obvious self-righteousness and—to Saunders—totally misplaced vehemence.

'Come along, Saunders.'

And Saunders did, flinching as she was forced to pass close to the man in order to get through the door, feeling like a racalcitrant schoolgirl and as angry with herself for having that feeling as she was with Charlotte for creating such a scene in the first place.

She had to trot to keep up with her friend's long-legged stride through the building's enormous lobby, still bustling with after-lunch crowds returning to the hundreds of offices that must, she thought, be enclosed within this building that loomed with herds of other glass-eyed giants in the centre of the city.

I am *not* enjoying this, she thought. She hadn't much enjoyed lunch, either; too much too rich food, too many glasses of the very good white wine Charlotte had insisted on. And, she was becoming increasingly convinced, too much Charlotte!

She wasn't like this when we were at school together, Saunders had thought, only to amend that as memory sharpened with use and she remembered that nursing-school Charlotte: the lean and lanky, testy, abrasive girl she'd roomed with through their entire nursing education, the banner-waver, the rebel.

As they marched across the lobby of the building, Charlotte leading and Saunders, a full head shorter, struggling to keep up, memories of those halcyon days kept getting mixed up with far more recent, far more disruptive memories. . .of eyes like black fire that snapped and crackled, of shoulders so broad they would have filled the doorway had the man not politely stepped aside, only to be roundly abused by Charlotte.

'Was all that really necessary? The man was only being polite, after all.'

They were in the lift now, and by some stroke of amazing good fortune were alone. Had there been others with them, Saunders thought she wouldn't have dared ask the question, lest it start off another round of Charlotte's feminist ravings and even further embarrassment for herself.

As it was, she was able to weather the storm with an almost contemplative calm, meeting her friend's bright green eyes with her own dark blue ones, smiling her own sweet-tempered, placid smile in response to her friend's fiery outburst.

I'd not realised how thin and angry Charlotte's mouth is, she found herself thinking, and then, irrelevantly, caught a mental picture of *his* mouth, twisting into that sneer, but a broad, generous, mobile mouth for all that—a mouth more accustomed to smiling.

What a silly comparison. But then she'd been making strange comparisons all the morning long, most of them between herself and Charlotte, most of them of questionable value.

Little, it seemed, remained of the two young women who'd taken their nursing training together. One had matured and gone on and on, upwardly mobile in the extreme, to become Charlotte, a green-eyed, fire-haired feminist who—according to her—almost single-handedly ran the medical assessment division of one of the country's largest travel insurance companies. Power-dressing, power breakfasts, power lunches. . . power everything, according to Charlotte. Fantastic money, world travel, lurks, perks and. . .power.

And herself, Saunders White, at thirty-three a nurse-administrator of a large and thriving regional diabetes centre, with a staff almost as large as that which Charlotte commanded, but no lurks or perks—only a comfortable wage, and nothing she would call power. And no world travel either; she was lucky to see the local beach at weekends.

But at least it hasn't turned me into a radical feminist, she found herself thinking, even as she nodded understanding—a nod Charlotte clearly interpreted as agreement.

Until Saunders asked, 'But what, really, did you accomplish? Except, of course, to make a splendid scene!'

'I put him in his place, didn't I? Chauvinist pig!'

Did you? Saunders didn't ask *that* question out loud; indeed, she tried very hard to be sure it didn't even emerge from her eyes. The last thing she wanted was to ruin the last remaining hour of this reunion; enough that she hadn't seen Charlotte in almost ten years without it all ending in a screaming row. But she knew, and privately she thought Charlotte a fool if she didn't know, that the tirade hadn't put *that* man in his place. It had made him angry, perhaps even furious, but it certainly hadn't altered either his attitudes or his opinions.

Instead of saying so, however, she put on her most placid face, the mental shield she had developed during those early years of nursing, and emerged from the lift with Charlotte to ooh and aah over her friend's large, luxurious office, with its computers and modems and vast array of telephones and hardly any paperwork at all.

How different from her own cramped quarters, she thought. Her office was filled with paper—pamphlets and leaflets and booklets and the host of other paraphernalia that she needed for her work. There was no plush carpet on her floor; hers was second-hand. The centre was itself second-hand—a former section of a much larger hospital complex—and it was filled with second-hand desks, second-hand chairs, cast-offs and left-overs from more readily funded areas of the hospital.

But the people weren't second-hand, and Saunders took some measure of satisfaction in that. They mightn't dress as elegantly as those she saw moving through Charlotte's realm, but her people were tops in their fields: nurse-educators, a specialist dietitian, a podiatrist, ancillary staff. And every single one of them dedicated, professional and splendid at what they did. A team, she thought. A good, hard-working, competent and happy group of specialists doing good and worthwhile work.

Charlotte, she decided, did not look happy. Not in the same way she, herself, felt happy about her job, her work, her career. There was a brittleness about her old friend, a brittleness clearly revealed in the outburst downstairs, in the way she seemd so bent on convincing Saunders just how happy she was! Funny way to show it—abusing some stranger for merely being polite, she thought.

It would take more than you, my girl, to put *that* man in his place, Saunders found herself thinking again, and was surprised at how the incident had stuck in her mind.

The incident? Or the man himself? Those questions came to mind when she finally left Charlotte and made her way out through the expanse of the lobby to where another man, an older, quite different man, showed *his* manners by holding the door for her and even offering a slight, courtly nod of his head as he did so.

Saunders smiled her thanks, spoke her thanks, and the incident put a spring in her step as she walked to the underground parking garage where she'd left her diminutive Mazda after the long trek to the city that morning. But it was the first man's face that hovered in her mind.

It had been such a strong face, not especially handsome but certainly striking, with that slightly greying hair against the dark, out-of-doors tan. A nice face, she decided. A face that had been lived in, that he was comfortable with. A face that without the fierceness might have been even more interesting, might have told her more about the man inside it. And those eyes!

'I wish it had been you at the door the second time,' she said aloud, then shook her wild mop of never-yet-manageable hair and laughed at the silliness of walking down the street talking to herself.

Still, it would have been nice. At least then she might have countered that baleful glare, that fierce look of contempt he'd shot her. And why *her*? She hadn't uttered a word during the entire incident, and if she had spoken it would have been in his defence. Not that he needed defending; that man could look after himself. It had seemed strange, though, that he had never uttered a word during the entire drama. No objection, no argument, no totally justified retort. He'd merely looked at Charlotte with something that could have been amusement, or dismay, or utter disdain. Or all three. And the way he'd looked at Saunders herself! Strange. . .

He wasn't a city person. Dressed for the city, certainly, and well-dressed too; his suit had been custom-tailored for him, would have to have been, judging from the width of those shoulders. And, from her one brief attempt just to stare at the floor and try to wish herself out of the scene, she remembered gleaming leather dress-boots below trousers with creases so sharp he might have shaved with them.

But he didn't wear that gear every day. Not with those work-toughened hands. Well cared for hands, but not those of an office worker.

'I doubt he'd suit the office, Clancy of the Overflow,' she trilled aloud, and laughed at the inanity of singing Banjo Patterson's poetry while negotiating the stark, soulless canyons of the city.

But driving home, after she'd negotiated the dense traffic and was out past the suburbs to where there was some greenery, and with some feeling of relief at being away from the hectic traffic and more hectic people, she stuck a cassette into the little car's tape-deck and breezed along the highway, listening to 'Clancy of the Overflow' and 'The Man from Snowy River', enjoying her drive now, and the music with it.

Except when she thought of those burning eyes and found herself wishing she'd had the decency to apologise for Charlotte, the sense to explain that *she* didn't share that radical feminism, that *she* appreciated good manners.

'And that I'm a people-pleaser who wants everybody to like me,' she admitted aloud, neither proud nor ashamed of the fact.

Saunders had long ago come to terms with the fact that she was a people-pleaser; indeed she was content with it, most of the time. Only when somebody had deliberately taken advantage, when she had *allowed* herself to be used because she hadn't thought quickly enough, had been too trusting, did that aspect of her character bother her just a trifle.

And that didn't happen all that often any more. Hardly at all, she had to admit, since the deaths of her parents. Both of them had been the worst abusers of her gentle nature, playing on their ailments—both real and imagined—sometimes so blatantly that it was difficult to believe they had even realised their only daughter was a nurse, was not taken in by their subterfuges, was not fooled.

'Not fooled. . .just too easy-going,' she said aloud. 'And it's something you really ought to watch, Saunders White, because all it ever does is give you more work and more hassles you didn't need in the first place.'

If she had been Charlotte, she thought, she obviously wouldn't be worried about people-pleasing. Nobody with the gumption to go about bashing a perfect stranger over the head with feminist principles could care that much about what people thought.

'And there was just no reason for it; that's what I can't get over,' she muttered, talking to herself as she often did on long drives. 'All the man did was exhibit normal, proper manners. Well, better than normal, if the truth be told. But *proper* manners; he did what he thought was expected of him—no, what *he* expected of himself! And then to have Charlotte start in on him. . .

'I just wonder why he didn't say anything. Strange, that. Not a single word. He hardly even bothered to look at her, mostly because he was looking at *me*— glaring at me as if it was all my fault, as if I'd put her up to it or something. What did he think, I wonder?'

She drove on for a bit in silence, then, pondering.

He had been so decidedly, deliciously, totally masculine, a man completely comfortable in his own
sexuality.

And, however, angry he might have been, he'd
looked at her as a woman—skinny, perhaps, but a
woman for all that. There had been something in those
incredible eyes that left her in no doubt about it.

'But he never said a word,' she told the white lines
that flashed towards her windscreen. 'And why me? I
still can't figure that bit out. If he'd given Charlotte
the dressing-down she deserved, or even just walked
away. . . But just to stand there and take it, and
glower at *me*. . .'

I should have just walked away, the man was thinking,
strong fingers drumming at the steering-wheel of his
four-wheel-drive station wagon as he rolled along the
same highway as Saunders, unaware of her presence a
kilometre behind him, but unable quite to forget her
presence at the incident earlier that day.

Now, as then, only half his mind was occupied with
thoughts of the moment, the rest was stubbornly
wrestling with the delemma so unexpectedly dumped
in his lap by his doctor earlier that morning.

I should have just walked away, he thought again.
Or else I should have taught that snooty feminist a few
new words and *then* walked away.

He grinned at the thought, the gesture revealing
strong, even teeth behind a well-formed, mobile
mouth. Just what words he might have taught
Charlotte became a subject of some conjecture; there
were few in today's society that even infants didn't
know.

Besides, there had been that other woman, the silent

one with the enormous deep blue eyes and that air of. . .vulnerability? No, he decided, not really vulnerability. A sort of gentleness, not passive, but somehow soothing. At least, to his eyes.

'Skinny, but. Wants a bit of feeding up—round off some of those sharp edges,' he muttered to himself.

And the way she had just stood there, gamely meeting his angry glare although for some reason silent herself. As if she had wanted to detach herself from the scene, had wanted to be somewhere else.

She hadn't approved; somehow he was certain of that, without really knowing how he knew. She hadn't approved, but had't wanted to make even more of a scene by taking sides. A fence-sitter?

Ford Landell hoped not; he had little time for people who tried to sit on fences, who wouldn't make a stand even when they held strong opinions. He, himself, was admittedly opinionated, even more admittedly a person who tended to back up his opinions with whatever action was required.

'I should have done *something*,' he said aloud, aware that he was talking to himself, annoyed because he considered that a bad habit he had never been able to break.

Actually, he had been about to speak out when his attention had been caught by the feminist's striking companion. His attitude had been a mixture of annoyance, contempt and laughter; it was, he had thought, mildly amusing to be abused for simple good manners.

But then he had seen *her*.

'And almost certainly never will again, so why I bother even thinking about it, I can't imagine,' he went on, aloud. 'Don't even know what was so special about her.'

Whatever it had been, he decided, it wasn't about to be put into words; he couldn't define it and didn't really want to. But neither, despite the unlikelihood of ever seeing the blue-eyed woman again, could he quite forget her either. He could only wish, as he did now, that they could have met—properly met—in different circumstances.

CHAPTER TWO

'I'M SENDING you a man.'

The voice was unmistakable, syrup-thick and unashamedly, irrevocably Irish. And deliberately provocative.

'But what would I do with it?' Saunders replied, not bothering to hide the delight in her voice. 'I couldn't afford to feed it, and they're terribly difficult to train.'

She hadn't heard from Dr Peter Mahoney in months; indeed, had wondered if her favourite general practitioner had finally worked himself to death or drink or both. They had done their training at the same hospital, and, if Peter hadn't been married already, Saunders had often said she'd have grabbed him for herself. She and Peter's wife Gail, while not close friends, liked each other and got on very well.

'This one is long past training, I do fear,' was the reply. 'Which is why I'm sending him along to you, dear Saunders. I'm hoping your own wondrous temperament can accomplish miracles.'

Saunders laughed, then sobered at the vibes she detected in his voice.

'That bad?'

Just occasionally, a person diagnosed with diabetes proved incapable of coming to terms with the situation, looming on the whole thing as some sort of divine retribution or something. It made the job of educating them to control their diabetes—and their lives—to achieve a more or less normal lifestyle very difficult indeed.

'Oh, probably not. But on the other hand. . .' Peter's voice trailed off as he drifted into thoughts perhaps best unsaid, Saunders thought, realising at the same time that they *must* be said, if only to give her something to work with.

'You're hedging,' she said. 'What's the problem—is he allergic to insulin, or afraid of the sight of his own blood?'

She kept the joshing tone in her voice, but was already making angry little doodles on her scratch-pad. Peter Mahoney was perhaps the finest general practitioner she knew, and if he was worried, *she* definitely ought to be.

'Afraid of absolutely nothing; that's the problem. Not even of me!' was the reply. 'Intelligent, able, but just so damned. . .pig-headed and independent. . .'

'Like his doctor,' Saunders couldn't help replying.

'Hell no! Ten times worse; a thousand times worse,' was the response. And she noted there was less of a note of humour in his voice than she might have expected.

'Well, then, why send him to me? Honestly, Peter, if you can't handle him, I don't see how you'd expect me to.'

Which had nothing to do with it, and Saunders knew that. Like any good GP, Peter Mahoney was reason-ably versed on diabetes and the various complications involved with it, but he was no specialist. In this region of the state, she was more the specialist than he, in the sense that, once diagnosed, diabetes was a lifetime condition requiring day-to-day management in which the patient's own involvement was crucial to any hope of success. Knowledge was the essential key, and her job was to give the diabetic that knowledge and help put it to work.

'I'm sending him because I send *all* my diabetic patients to you, as you well know. The reason I'm phoning to warn you is only that this boyo might prove a touch more difficult than most.'

'Well, I can believe that, since by the way you're talking he certainly isn't in your consulting-room listening to you,' Saunders said. And then, with sudden alarm, 'Surely not?'

'Of course not. I picked it up, actually, as part of a general check-up, and he's away now getting dressed. I only wanted to be sure of an appointment time, is all.'

Saunders consulted her diary: Thursday, now, and tomorrow booked solid and into overtime because of the afternoon she'd taken off yesterday to lunch with Charlotte. Monday no better.

'It will have to be first thing Tuesday,' she finally said. 'Would nine o'clock be all right?'

'He'll be there, if I have to drag him personally,' was the reply. 'Although to be sure I'd hoped you might be able to make it sooner. Still. . .'

The doctor then launched into providing Saunders with the minimum details she would require, promising that a proper letter of referral would accompany his patient. She noted the man's particulars without paying particular attention; the success of his treatment, both she and Peter knew, would depend more on the man himself than on the specifics of the symptoms.

Still. . . Fordon Landell; forty-one, six feet tall, eighty-one kilos, self-employed mining consultant and engineer. Diagnosed. . .yesterday, she realised; Peter had obviously called him in this morning for the appropriate glucose testing.

As if reading her thoughts, the doctor said, 'They couldn't do the test—his blood sugar level was fifteen point four after fasting, if you can imagine it. I suspect a lot of that was inner stress, but. . .'

Just within the right age-group, hardly overweight at that height, but given his symptoms. . .

'The expectable nightly wanderings,' Peter said, not bothering to use the proper medical terminology of polyuria with Saunders. 'General feeling of malaise, poor concentration, dry mouth. I tested him here at over twelve and there's no doubt.'

Certainly not, she thought. Type 2 diabetes—technically described as non-insulin-dependent diabetes mellitus—by far the most common form of diabetes, touching one person in sixty in the over-thirty age-group. Distinctly hereditary, far more so than the insulin-dependent variety which usually struck younger people.

'History?' The question was automatic, because of the strong hereditary factor. Given one parent with this form of diabetes, the chance of inheritance was about one in ten; if both parents had the malady, the risk doubled.

'I'll let him discuss that with you; it's a bit complicated,' Peter replied, then swiftly moved on to other elements of the diagnosis. Saunders accepted the evasiveness without comment.

After Peter had hung up, she scanned her brief notes, then filed them away to await Mr Landell's Tuesday appointment. The doctor's warnings didn't really change much; she would have to deal with

Fordon Landell as she did with all her other clients, with an approach custom-tailored to suit the individual.

Saunders knew her greatest single advantage in her chosen work was intangible, something it was difficult even to put into words sometimes. It was easiest described as a natural empathy, something most good nurses had to a greater or lesser degree, but which Saunders possessed to an uncanny extent. She could usually pick up people's feelings and emotions almost as easily as she could read a printed page, and some quality within her allowed her to respond in a way that provided reassurance and comfort far beyond anything she could say in words.

As a young nurse, this empathy had sometimes caused problems; she had been prone to becoming too personally involved with patients, too close to their very real if often irrational fears and concerns. But maturity had eventually provided the judgement and experience to manage her talent with the proper mix of empathy and reality, so that she was protected from potential abuse of her warm nature.

A friend who was involved in politics had once declared it the finest natural bulldust detector he'd ever seen; Saunders hadn't had the heart to enlighten him about just how much work had gone into the learning. Nor, for that matter, how often she still got led astray by her empathy.

There were times she needed all her talents and all the luck she could possibly muster, and the arrival of Fordon Landell on Tuesday morning was defintely, beyond question, one of them!

Saunders was having a quick word in passing with

one of the junior nurse-educators, and had her back to the entryway, when she heard him announce himself at Reception.

He's punctual, anyway, she thought to herself with a glance at her wristwatch to find him five minutes early. Saunders turned round and walked towards Reception, still looking at her watch and forming a greeting in her mind. Then she looked up and the words stalled in her throat as she met coal-black eyes that seemed to flare with a truly devilish glee before that fleeting impression subsided into bleak, black emptiness.

'Mr. . . Mr. . . Landell?'

She managed, finally, to get that much out, feeling as if her throat was bloated, swollen.

His reply was a curt, barely-perceptible nod.

'Yes. . . Well. . . I'm. . . Saunders White,' she said. 'Won't you. . .umm. . .come into my office, please?'

One dark eyebrow was raised in an expression that could have meant anything from agreement to amusement, but as she turned away she *knew* he was behind her, knew it without having to listen for his silent footsteps on the worn carpet. He might as well have been holding on to her, she was so aware of his presence.

But it was even worse when they reached the office doorway and she automatically held the door open with one hand, gesturing him to enter the room. He said nothing, merely inclined his head a trifle and raised that eyebrow again. But the devils laughed in his eyes now! Saunders didn't even have to look at him to know that. As he moved towards the indicated chair, and she to her desk, memory of that earlier encounter in the city flooded back to colour her cheeks and clamp a stutter on to her tongue.

And, once seated, his briefcase on the floor at his feet, he clearly wasn't about to make things any easier for her. He made no effort to bring up the subject of their earlier encounter, thus giving her no chance at all to explain her side of it. And yet. . .she couldn't help feeling that he somehow expected *her* to make some effort in that direction.

And I won't, she thought, struggling beneath the directness of his gaze to reassert her authority and composure. It was, after all, *her* office.

She forced herself to meet his gaze squarely, willing her mind into the beginnings of the usual spiel about diet and exercise and their importance in the scheme of things.

Fordon Landell listened in silence, making no attempt to interrupt, but never taking his eyes from her either. If only, she thought, it was possible to be certain he was actually *listening*.

The fierceness of his stare made it increasingly difficult for Saunders, and she finally wound down, unable to read his mood or to get any vibes at all from him. For the first time ever, her sensitivity to others was letting her down.

'I've got a few specific questions, if this is the time for them,' he said when she paused. 'Unless you'd rather finish your bit first?'

'No, you go ahead,' she said, and leaned back in her chair, relieved finally to be able to get *some* reaction from this extraordinary man.

He hefted the briefcase and methodically laid out in front of him the latest books available, she knew, on the subject of diabetes.

What followed was a quizzing that revealed to Saunders just how quickly and thoroughly this man had researched the subject in the short time available to him. His questions were sensible, pertinent and specific, and the way he approached things told her a good deal more about him than he might have realised.

Peter Mahoney hadn't been exaggerating. Fordon Landell clearly had no fears about his diabetes; if anything he was too unafraid. Saunders divined from his attitude that he intended to face the problem as he did all others—head-on and with all the common sense and logic he could muster. And, at whatever cost, *he* would be in control. Except. . .

'I'm sorry to tell you that this may not all be quite that simple,' she had to say. And watched those black, black eyes go even darker, saw determination firm up an already too-firm chin.

'Meaning?'

'Meaning. . .just what I said,' she replied, cautious now, not wishing to offend him deliberately, but wanting to try and reach some genuinely common ground for discussion.

'I have the feeling you're looking at the problem as something you can. . .just solve; something you can find a distinct, obvious, permanent solution for.' And she waved her hands in a square, boxy pattern in the air, as if she, too, could put the issue into an easily definable framework.

'And you don't think I can?'

Those unfathomable eyes seemed to flicker, but whether with anger or amusement she couldn't tell. All Saunders wished was for him to stop devouring her with them.

'I *know* you can't,' she replied, forcing calm into her

voice, trying at the same time to still the fluttering in her tummy, the quickening of her pulse.

Damn the man! He was deliberately setting out to stir her up, and he was clever and subtle enough to do it without actually doing *anything*, or, at least, nothing she could respond against without leaving herself wide open to ridicule. . .or worse.

'What, exactly, is it that you're trying to accuse me of?' he asked. 'Do you reckon that I'm too stupid to understand all this bumph—' with a sweeping gesture towards the books he'd brought with him'—or that I'm just not going to comply amiably with *your* every rule?'

Saunders couldn't help but smile. Now, she thought, we're getting somewhere.

'I don't offer you any rules, Mr Landell,' she said. 'You're the only person who can set the rules involved with your diabetes. Or rather your body will, if that makes sense to you.'

'My body doesn't seem to have done such a crash-hot job so far,' he replied, with a grin that didn't extend past that mobile mouth. His eyes remained calm, cool, watchfully aware, even cautious.

'What you're saying. . .what you *seem* to be saying,' she corrected herself quickly, 'is that you feel your body has rather let you down. That isn't the best attitude to take, if you don't mind me saying so.'

She paused, waiting for an interjection that didn't come, then went on.

'There simply is no logic in blaming your body for the fact you've developed diabetes. Or in blaming bad luck, or fate, or God, or. . .whatever. Given your age and the fact that you're hardly what I would describe as overweight, it's more than likely that about the only thing you *might* blame is heredity, and there isn't a lot of sense in that—not in the long run.'

He shrugged, and Saunders detected in that gesture more than just simple lack of interest.

'Maybe a good, handy scapegoat is better than none at all?' he said.

'Only if you're the kind of person who needs one.'

She kept her voice carefully neutral, implying neither that she thought he might be, nor the opposite. She didn't dare to voice the feeling she had, which was that this man had never needed a scapegoat for anything, and wasn't about to start now.

And, as if reading her mind, he grinned—this time a genuine, warm, *human* grin.

'OK, let's stop fencing about that one,' he said. 'I've read everything I could get my hands on over the weekend, and I do know there's no sense playing who's-to-blame games. And I have to admit also, Miss White, that you've answered my questions with a bit more. . .directness?. . .than I've given you. There could very well be a strong hereditary element in my case; the point is that I simply don't know. Nor have I any way of finding out.'

Saunders thought she had become rather good at hiding her instinctive reactions, but she must have registered something, because he raised one eyebrow slightly, then continued.

'I'm an orphan.' The statement was uttered without emotion or bitterness—surprisingly, she thought, considering his next remark.

'I was abandoned on the steps of the Launceston General Hospital in Tasmania, in the middle of what I'm told was my first night in this world.'

'How——' Saunders started to say, 'how awful', but

choked back the remark as Fordon Landell's eyes seemed to flash reproach at the pity.

He shrugged.

'Could have been worse, couldn't it? Diabetes that my. . .mother probably couldn't have predicted isn't much compared with a lot of other health problems she could have left me with.'

'Well, that's certainly true, although. . .'

She let the sentence die. What use, indeed, even to think about comparisons with babies being born the world over with far worse problems?

'Although, of course, it must influence my *own* parenting plans,' he prompted, seemingly unaware that he had just—conveniently—changed the subject for her.

'To a degree, I suppose,' Saunders said, after a moment's thought in which Fordon Landell's direct, unswerving gaze made thinking more difficult than she liked to admit. 'But, really, mature onset diabetes can hardly compare in seriousness with a lot of hereditary conditions.'

He didn't reply, so, after another endless silence, she continued, 'And, of course, many people have their children, even their grandchildren, before they ever know they have diabetes, or even that it might exist in their families.'

'Hardly an excuse I'm eligible to use now.'

I can't imagine you stooping to excuses, she thought, but only nodded her reply.

'And, because I don't know the. . .circumstances of my heredity, it makes any sort of prediction a bit iffy anyway, doesn't it?'

'And that's going to be a problem for you, isn't it?' Saunders asked, although she knew the answer already. Her empathetic antennae had suddenly switched on, reaching out as if to touch physically this man's innate craving for a large family of his own. It wasn't surprising, given the circumstances, but the intensity of the feelings he radiated was almost over-whelmingly strong.

'Is it that obvious?'

He didn't seem perturbed by her perception; nor did he seem ill-at-ease with the strength of his own emotions. But the aura of strength that emanated from his seemingly relaxed posture was contradictory, confusing.

Saunders broke away from his glance, looking down at her notes in a frantic bid to dissemble.

'You're. . .not married, I see,' she finally said, in lieu of being able to find any more sensible comment.

'Nor have I been, which at least means I'm spared any embarrassing explanations thus far,' was the reply. Casual; far too casual.

'But you've been thinking about it, and now you've changed your mind?'

The words slipped out even as Saunders thought them, thinking to herself and only aware she'd spoken aloud when she saw the warning flashes in those black eyes.

But when he replied, with hardly any perceptible hesitation, it was only to say, again too casually, 'Well, you're half-right, anyway.'

And if you think I'm going to ask which half, then think again, Mr Fordon Landell, Saunders thought to herself, keeping her mouth firmly shut in case she might again let something slip out.

He ignored her discomfort, if he even noticed it.

'It does present an interesting problem, though,' he

mused, almost as if he was speaking to himself. 'I mean, at what point in a relationship do you tell somebody you've got a hereditary defect? The real significance of which you have no way of kowing but "just in case you *do* want children, my dear". . .'

His tone was casual, but his eyes mocked her.

Saunders refused to be baited.

'If it were me, I'd be more worried just now with——' she began, only to be interrupted.

'If it were you? Let us assume it is, Miss White,' he said, and there was that hint of mockery in his voice now, that undertone of warning. 'Let us assume it *is* you with this. . .this geriatric onset diabetes.' And now his voice was clearly mocking, although she couldn't be sure if the mockery was aimed at her or at himself. 'At what point in a relationship would *you* bring up the subject, and how would you do it?'

'You really are making much too much of this,' she began, but he shook his head, raising a finger to his nose in admonishment.

'And *you* are being evasive.'

Evasive? If only he knew, Saunders thought. And then, suddenly, almost terrifyingly, realised that he *would* know, and almost certainly he would know in the next few minutes. Because she was going to tell him. She didn't know why she knew it, and she certainly didn't know *why* she would tell him, but she would!

'It's not a matter of being evasive.'

'Well. . .?'

'It's just that you *are* making far too much of it,' she insisted.

'Which, of course, is the only reason you refuse just

to give me a plain and simple answer to a plain and simple question.'

'I'm not refusing,' she denied. 'I merely said that there are other, more important priorities you should be thinking about just now.'

'How do you know?'

'I. . . Well. . .I'm just assuming. . .'

'Just assuming I haven't got a particular girl in mind right this very minute?' he countered. 'That, it seems to me, is quite an assumption, Miss White. For all you know I'm on the very threshold of becoming engaged, or married. On the very lip of the abyss, so to speak. . .yea and verily doomed to domesticity.'

Which would have been a perfectly acceptable counter if only he hadn't suddenly started looking at her in that way. Whatever *that* way was, she thought, half-angry, but not sure if it was with herself or this insufferably arrogant, far too perceptive man.

'Being a diabetic does *not* mean you can't, or shouldn't, have children!' she snapped. 'Non-insulin-dependent diabetes does not miraculously transform to insulin-dependent diabetes through heredity; they are two markedly different conditions.'

But now that I have it, the heredity factor rears its ugly head—does it not?'

'Now that you *know* you have it—yes! But still, all you would—might—pass on is the propensity for the same type of diabetes you yourself have. And there is no guarantee that you would, anyway. You've read the books; surely you know that?'

'I *know* only that, for all I know, it could run like a chain through the last fifteen generations of my family on both sides,' he retorted, and for the first time she detected a note of definite, undeniable anger.

'And you also know, or so I presume, that *anybody* can get diabetes. Anybody!'

She was getting angry herself now, angry at how this man could so easily get under her skin.

'And the two types of diabetes are clinically and genetically distinct. Even if you married a girl with Type 1 diabetes, it wouldn't increase your childrens' chances of developing the type *you* have.'

Saunders fought to keep her voice from rising, fought to keep Fordon Landell from realising just how stirred up she had become.

'If the girl you marry has insulin-dependent diabetes, you'll almost certainly know it beforehand; if she's going to develop Type 2, as you have, pregnancy could bring it on, or not; age could bring it on, or not; any combination of factors could affect the situation. The point is, she might end up with diabetes anyway, and have no more idea where it came from than you do.'

'Absolutely none of which alters the fact that I shall have to discuss the matter with any girl I might decide to marry,' he insisted, eyes bleak, attitude implacable.

'Well, so what? I can think of a thousand worse things to find out about a prospective husband, and so could any other woman with half the brains God gave a brown dog.'

Saunders shook her head, then, and abruptly looked up and smiled in surprise at her own over-reaction.

'How on earth did this discussion get so heated?' she asked, the question aimed more at herself than at Fordon Landell. 'It just isn't that big an issue; it really isn't!'

'Easy enough for you to say,' was the reply, in a voice still alive with tension. 'Even discounting the fact that diabetes presents some very specific risks in pregnancy—and yes, Miss white, I *have* read about that too—you still haven't answered my original question. How would you fancy having to tell your husband-to-be that you suffered from diabetes?'

'It wouldn't be a problem, Mr Landell,' she replied in a voice now equally caustic. 'It wouldn't be any problem at all, because, Mr Landell, I don't *suffer* from diabetes—I *control* my diabetes.

'And that,' she said, with eyes as narrow with anger as his were wide with surprise, 'is what *you* should be worrying about—*controlling* your diabetes instead of fretting over the trivialities of potential hereditary problems.

'I pity the girl you do marry, Mr Landell, because if she has hair the colour of yours and your children turn out to be redheads, they—and *she*—will be more likely to suffer from your misplaced logic and probable insane jealousy than they will from having to worry about getting diabetes when they're older.'

Consider yourself *told*, boy, Ford thought, and well and truly told, at that.

He sat immobile, determined not to reveal to this astonishing woman how effective her outburst had really been.

Certainly, he thought, it was too late by half to reveal that he had only been stirring, that he had no immediate objective in mind, no woman whose future would be affected in the slightest by his thoughts on the genetics of the situation.

Until now—and there was no way he'd tell her *that*!

He knew himself, perhaps only too well. Which, of course, meant that he knew she was consistent and correct in her assessment of him. He wasn't looking at the problem of his diabetes as a lifelong situation that would require lifelong control; he was—had been—looking at it as a probelm to be *solved*, something he could fix.

And, worse, just the thought of having to face it *her* way was. . .difficult. It wasn't his way; it demanded an acceptance he wasn't sure at this point in time he could manage, although already he was adjusting to the fact that accept it he must.

And with that acceptance came another, the acceptance—and this one was easy, perhaps too easy—that this was a woman he might want to mother his children, to share his life. The knowledge of this struck at him virtually without warning; one moment he was rationally aware of her attractiveness, which had struck him so visibly during their first encounter in the city, the next he was quite irrationally aware of her subtle strength, her gentle but now obvious resilience, her. . . completeness.

Ford Landell took a slow, deep breath and eased back slightly in his chair, forcing an illusion of calm despite the sudden emotions that raged through him, forcing, he thought with grim irreverence, his blood sugar to what were probably alarming readings.

CHAPTER THREE

SAUNDERS watched as those midnight eyes, impossible
as it seemed, grew even darker. Watched them darken
and at the same time flare in flecks of colour, remind-
ing her of a fabulous black opal she'd once seen and
lusted after.

Lusted after. . . That thought did nothing to
improve her awe at being so provocatively outspoken.
Neither did Fordon Landell's implacable silence, a
silence so profound she fancied she could hear both
their hearts beating in the stillness of the room.

Fordon Landell had shifted back in his chair at her
outburst, almost as if she had physically slapped his
face, and now whatever empathetic link she had held
with him was gone; she couldn't read those eyes, could
discover nothing in his deliberately blank expression.
But at least there was no question about his paying
attention. She fancied she could almost *hear* his mind
churning over what she had said and what reply he
would—eventually—make.

'I must apologise; I don't usually get quite so carried
away,' she finally said. Meaning it, of course, but also
desperate for anything to break the torture of the
silence in the small room. It was like being caged with
a lion and watching it silently deciding whether to be
hungry or not.

'I can't imagine why,' was the surprising reply. 'I'm
the one who should be apologising, if anyone should.

34

You actually showed remarkable restraint, considering the way I was pushing.'

One powerful hand ruffled through the coarse shock of frosted ink hair, while at the same time his eyes softened, lost that sharp edge of. . .of what? Defensiveness? Wariness? Hostility? Saunders found she was no longer sure, if she ever had been.

'It's just that. . . Well. . .having found out about this diabetes, and the almost certainty in my case that it's hereditary, I guess I've been letting my imagination run riot a bit about what *else* there might be, lurking in my unknown genetics. . .'

His voice ran down, and as it did so Saunders began once again to pick up his emotional vibes. She was again amazed at how strongly this happened, at how attuned she became to him—so quickly—once he let down his guard.

'That's a natural enough reaction,' she said, moved to compassion by how worried he had let himself become, at how fiercely he felt about the potential problems his past might provide for his future—and for his children's.

'But really, Mr Landell, it's. . .it's just not something you *can* worry about. Not that way. You just can't accomplish anything but more worry—unnecessary worry—and when it comes to controlling your diabetes, you must consider that avoiding stress and unnecessary worry is very, very important.'

Saunders paused, but he made no attempt to interject.

'The point is,' she finally continued,'that you haven't got a disease. Diabetes, especially our sort of diabetes, isn't a disease, exactly—it's a condition; it can't be cured, like most diseases, or *not* cured, like those they haven't found a cure for yet. But it can be managed, controlled.

'I like to think of it as a lifestyle condition,' she said then, and brightened her tone, not deliberately, but as if in some response to. . .to what? Something in this man's attitude, she was certain, but just exactly what, she couldn't determine. She went on, wondering if she was reacting to the shifting light in his expression at her earlier use of the term 'our'. Or just to the man himself.

Because the major factors in managing diabetes, in *controlling* the condition, are essentially the same as those required for any healthy lifestyle—get fit and stay fit, eat the right kinds of food at the right times. Diet and exercise—those are the two keys to control. Diet and exercise.'

Now it was her turn to run down. To her own ears, Saunders was starting to sound like a used-car salesman extolling the virtues of a questionable bargain. It was no real surprise to see a glint of humour in Fordon Landell's dark eyes, although when he finally spoke, one dark eyebrow raised in tune with his attitude, she was a bit surprised at his astuteness.

'Have you ever considered a career in politics, Miss White? You have all the makings of a *mighty* snake-oil salesman.'

But he was smiling now. And there had been no acid in his words, no air of hostility or resentment. He was laughing *with* her now, not *at* her.

And also, she realised, laughing at himself. Although she could not be certain, at first, if it was the healthy laughter of a balanced individual or if there was still that tinge of acid bitterness she had earlier found in his words.

'That is what my job is all about,' she finally replied. 'Selling people a new lifestyle and the tools to make it work—information, knowledge, sometimes a bit of reassurance. You could say, I suppose, that I'm something of a power-broker, Mr Landell, because with diabetes, knowledge is certainly power!'

He smiled at that, then asked, 'And does having the. . .lifestyle yourself make the job easier, or harder?'

'Easier, I guess, I was diagnosed at thirty-one, which is rather young, but it certainly wasn't as surprising to me as I expect your diagnosis was for you. My nursing training helped, of course, but heredity in my case was definitely a known factor. Both my parents had late-onset diabetes, and there is a long history of it on both sides of my family.'

She paused then, thoughtful. 'Both my parents died last year from the complications of their diabetes and both of them suffered greatly throughout their later lives because of it. Which is why I take rather great pride and pleasure in trying to help other diabetics to avoid that suffering.'

Something changed in his smoky eyes, something that reacted to the sadness she still felt at her parents' deaths, a sadness that existed even though she was more angry about their deaths than sad.

'That must have been a bit traumatic, if you had to go through their deaths and then come in here and reassure people the way you've tried to do with me. Or have you been using your own grief as a tool?'

The perceptiveness startled her. Of course she'd used her grief as a tool, but more than her grief she had used her anger, the rage she had felt every time either of her parents refused to face up to their responsibilities to themselves, to her, to. . .everything.

Fordon Landell was the first client she had ever told about having diabetes herself; even his doctor, her friend, didn't know. She was so used to living with the condition that she hardly noticed it any more. Until now. What, she wondered, had prompted her to reveal herself so readily to this stranger?

'More my anger than my grief,' she said. 'My parents were fools, the both of them. They simply would *not* make any attempt to control their diabetes as they should have, or to listen to me, or anybody else, for that matter. My father lost two toes to gangrene because he wouldn't stop smoking, wouldn't take proper care of himself, and my mother. . .my mother. . .'

She didn't realise the intensity of her own emotions until she noticed through her burgeoning tears the startled expression on Fordon Landell's face, until his long, strong fingers reached across her desk to take her hand, leaving her with only one hand free now to swipe at the tears as they welled out.

But she felt his empathy, felt his genuine warmth and compassion as if it was being transmitted through the fingers that now stroked her wrist in a silent communication that did more for her than any words could.

He remained silent throughout her sobbing, trembling catharsis, but his touch was soothing, steadying, strangely comforting. As was his silence; as reason returned she found herself thinking it was unusual, but nice, to meet a man who knew when *not* to try and use words to comfort.

'I. . . I must have needed that,' she finally said,

tugging free her wrist as her emotions came under control, and she suddenly realised that his touch was having other effects than comfort, that she was responding now to the gentle stroking of his fingers with a fluttery feeling in her tummy, a definite stirring of her pulse.

And he was aware of *that*, too! He released her wrist, but only to hold her with his eyes as she looked up at him, his glance creating an almost tangible chain between them. Saunders couldn't continue to meet those molten black eyes. She had to look away, tried to, couldn't, then didn't want to.

'I'd say you must have,' he replied, voice calm, gentle, still as reassuring as his touch had been earlier. And then, with an accuracy that for some reason didn't surprise her, added, 'And I suppose you spent until last year in a continuous battle with your parents, trying to get them to mend their ways?'

'For all the good it did any of us,' she said, not bothering now to try and hide the bitterness. 'I had originally intended to take up medicine; I'd always fancied being a doctor, or at least I did until I actually started working with doctors all the time and came to realise. . . Well. . . Anyway, that idea got rather side-tracked when I got into university and realised I was going to end up being the family bread-winner before I could ever think of getting through med school.'

'Nursing a second-best option?' And there was more to the question than just the words, but how much more Saunders couldn't quite determine.

'A best option, as it turned out. I'd have made a lousy doctor,' she replied with a half-smile. 'Actually, I now realise with the benefit of hindsight that I should have taken up teaching; on my better days I fancy I've actually got a flair for it. Or maybe it's just because I'm involved here in teaching about something I understand, something that's very important to me both personally and professionally. Speaking of which, I'm running out of time here and we still have a lot to cover, so if you don't mind. . .?'

'I am entirely at your command,' he said, inclining his silvery head in a gesture that would have seemed ludicrous in most men, but which he managed to carry off with a unique mixture of dignity and humour.

Saunders spent the rest of the appointment time explaining about blood glucose monitoring, fighting throughout to maintain her professional detachment and ignore the simple physical effect just touching him seemed to create.

When he rolled up the sleeve of his tartan shirt to allow her to fit the collar to test his blood pressure, she adjusted the strap around a muscular bicep that seemed to take on a life of its own under the touch of her fingers. His blood pressure was well within normal limits; her own was in serious question as she looked up from her reading to find his eyes calmly grazing along the lines of her throat and bosom.

He observed with sardonic detachment as she explained and demonstrated how to prick his finger with a lancet, how to 'milk' a drop of blood for analysis, how to check it against the colour chart on the indicator strip container.

He didn't flinch at the infinitesimal pricking of the lancet, but Saunders was certain it wasn't through any sense of false macho imagery. It was, she knew by her own reactions, at least in part due to the fact that he wasn't paying any attention to the tiny bit of pain; he was too busy watching her again.

While she, for the first time since she'd been a raw student nurse, found her own fingers trembling just a smidgen, and knew beyond question that it was a direct result of how she could feel his eyes on her, could feel a definite, undeniable undercurrent of blatant sexual attraction.

Which was reciprocated; she had to admit that to herself, even though all her instincts screamed at her to deny it. Not that there was much sense in that. Fordon Landell knew it as well as she, herself.

About the only saving grace was when she had used the lancet and had turned away to reach for a medicated swab for him to wipe his finger. She turned back to find him calmly licking away the excess blood, looking for all the world like a wayward child who'd come crying to mommy only to find that it didn't hurt any more after all.

When she was explaining the elements of the various available blood glucose monitoring machines, she *knew* somehow that this part of her spiel was probably wasted, at least for now. And wasn't at all surprised by his response.

'It may sound ridiculous, but I don't trust machines all that much. For now, I think, I'd prefer to trust my own eyes and judgement; I can always change my mind later.'

Saunders definitely did *not* consider herself a salesperson in this regard. She, herself, didn't use a glucometer, except when at work, where she had one handy anyway. But her blood sugar had been stabilised so well for so long that she hardly needed to test at all, except to keep in the habit. She was totally in tune with her body, or had been, she thought, until this man had come into the picture.

'You're going to have to test four times a day for a while,' she said. 'Peter. . . Dr Mahoney has you on the minimum dose of tablets, and it may work out that getting your diet and exercise patterns into proper balance will mean you can manage without any medication at all. *May*! You'll have to expect it to take up to three months for that to become clear, as I expect he's already told you. But, regardless of whether you take tablets or not, you must expect to monitor regularly, especially in the early stages.'

'First thing in the morning and before all meals. . . OK,' he said. 'And what, exactly, am I looking for? I've read about it, but I want to hear it from you; somehow I think it might register better coming from you.'

And his eyes said other things, intimate things, things Saunders both wanted to hear and didn't even want to think about. It was insane, she thought. Here she was, trying to educate him, sticking needles into him, and he was trying to seduce her at every step. Worse, she didn't know who was winning.

'Ideal control is three to six millimols before meals and no more than eight after meals—two hours after, but we'll come to that over time,' she replied, reciting the figures from memory and wishing he would stop *looking* at her that way. 'Now, our time for today is just about up, but before you go I want you to make an appointment for some time soon with Diane, our dietitian, and also with Yvonne, who's our podiatrist.'

'And with you?'

Such a simple question. Simple in words, but so complicated by the look in his eyes, just by the way he asked it, by the way he looked at her when he did!

Saunders had a momentary thought to switch him to

one of the junior nurse-educators, felt a curious tremor of confusion at the very thought. It was going to be dangerous dealing with Fordon Landell, everything in her instinct told her that. Besides, he didn't really need her particular talent of empathy and reassurance—he already understood power, had already determined to control his condition. This man had controlled his own life almost from the beinning; *he* wouldn't become one of those diabetics like her parents, who couldn't or wouldn't face up to reality, who insisted and kept on insisting that they were *sick*, as if that could automatically become the precursor to some miraculous cure.

'Well, you probably won't need to see me again quite that soon,' she replied. 'But, of course, if you have problems of any kind, I'm always available. . .'

She was stopped in her tracks there by the look of quiet satisfaction that flickered across his eyes, a look that might have been laughter, might have been just a trick of the light, but wasn't really either. It was, she found, a prelude to something far less easy to deal with.

'I don't suppose you'd accept an immediate plea that I just can't manage to monitor my own blood properly, and that it would be nice if *you* could do it for me?'

'No more than I'd accept that you can't manage to change your own socks,' she replied firmly, but the firmness was turned to a chuckle by his impish grin. He was having her on, deliberately flirting now, and making no real effort to conceal the fact.

Saunders deliberately glanced down at her wrist-watch, knowing his appointment was well into over-time, and only glad there was nobody being kept waiting by the situation. Fordon Landell, in tune with her thinking, took the hint.

She rushed through the rest of the preliminaries, lending him a packet of test strips until he could arrange his own supply through Diabetes Australia, giving him the various forms to be filled out to that purpose, running through the material in the pre-arranged folder of information on diet, the need to watch himself in case of the tablets driving him into a hypo—the low blood sugar condition of hypoglycaemia.

'It isn't a problem, really,' she explained. 'You'll quickly come to recognise the symptoms, and if you're in doubt, just gobble down a glucose tablet or a couple of jelly beans or something. Only remember to get some proper carbohydrates into you as quickly as possible afterwards, or the process will just repeat itself, because the sugar gets absorbed too fast and you're left with low blood sugar again.'

'I know we're getting into overtime here,' he replied, 'but I do have to worry about that aspect of things, as I've already mentioned. Much of the time I'm working alone, and a damned long way from any sort of help if I did need it. Should I be worried about that more than I am, or what?'

The ringing of her telephone interrupted Saunders' train of thought, and she answered to find her next appointment waiting, which didn't help.

'I think you should try to get in touch with your reactions fairly quickly,' she replied. 'The symptoms are sometimes a bit tricky, but once you've experienced a hypo or two, you'll recognise them readily enough. If it causes real problems, I'd get Peter. . . Dr Mahoney to think about changing your medication.

Considering the remote circumstances in which you work, it's worth considering, but I have to say also that it isn't my job to go about second-guessing your doctor. Doctors have a habit of getting quite narked by nurses who do that.'

'My old mate Peter, narked with a beautiful woman? I'd have to see that one myself to believe it,' was the reply, and Saunders shivered inside at the somehow special emphasis he put on that word 'beautiful'. She wasn't beautiful, and she knew it, but she was a woman, and as susceptible to flattery—even deliberately blatant flattery—as any other woman.

Fordon Landell knew *that*! Even at their most heated moments, during this hour and a bit that seemed far longer than that, he had been deliberately setting out to charm her, and both of them, she realised, knew he was succeeding beyond all logic.

Which was why she put up her mental and emotional shield; with this moment of his departure she was suddenly frightened by it all, by the quickness of her responses, by the apparent quickness of his responses. By the seemingly mutual attraction, the way his look could stir her, the way his touch could make her tummy turn over, her pulse race into oblivion. And there was no logic to it at all. At their first encounter in the city he'd seemed to hate her, had seemed. . .

'Why did you seem so angry with me during our. . . encounter in the city the other day?' she asked abruptly, the words out before she'd even realised it.

'Angry with you? I wasn't angry with you at all,' he replied immediately. 'I was a bit narked with your. . . friend, but very definitely not with you. Actually, I rather thought you were just about as embarrassed by the whole situation as I was.'

'But you hardly even looked at Charlotte,' Saunders protested, quite happy to accept his explanation but still a touch confused by it. 'And the way you were looking at me didn't indicate anything like sympathy over shared embarrassment.'

'I didn't waste much time looking at your friend because it was much more pleasant looking at you,' was the reply. 'In fact, looking at you was about the only saving grace in the entire performance.'

Which wasn't entirely the truth, Ford admitted to himself. When he had looked at Saunders, all thought of her friend and that woman's feminist nonsense had been driven from his head. But he wasn't about to tell her that.

Not now—now when his head was filled with other thoughts, still concerning this woman with the unusual name and equally unusual affect on him.

It seemed incredible, somehow, that all these thoughts about the hereditary aspects of diabetes had forced themselves into his head, that what had begun as a simple attempt to stir—or so he had thought at the time—now took on a quite different aspect, a quite different seriousness.

When he had first begun to read the various books available on the subject, the issue had been only one of many, and because he had not, then, even so much as thought about marriage, much less children, the issue had seemed almost irrelevant.

Until today, when it had sprung full-blown from his weary mind with an importance he couldn't have imagined. Just because of this woman? Just because of this small, too-slender, too-calming woman with the enormous dark blue eyes?

You want out of this, my lad, Ford Landell told himself. This woman is getting to you, and it's nothing you bargained for, nothing you're prepared to handle. He grinned, then, but only on the inside. It was also, he knew, too *late* to get out of it!

CHAPTER FOUR

THE nearest Saunders could find to park near the Mahoneys' luxurious home was almost two blocks away, leaving her an uphill journey into a biting wind that seemed bent on eroding her already fading enthusiasm for the visit.

She didn't really like large parties; only her doctor friend's insistence, and the fact that it was a Friday night—no work tomorrow—had convinced her to attend.

That, and. . . Oh, admit it, you goose, she told herself, gritting her teeth against a particularly nasty wind-gust, you might as well. But it did little for her enthusiasm to admit that the vague possibility Fordon Landell might also be there had been at least a consideration.

Admit too, she thought almost angrily, that, despite not having seen him since his visit to her office, his existence had been a seemingly constant intrusion into her thoughts.

'Woooweee! Isn't he just about the niftiest, most gorgeous *hunk* you've ever seen?'

Diane, the centre's dietitian, had fairly *floated* into Saunders' office after her first session with Fordon Landell, her entire being positively alight with interest.

'He. . .who?' Saunders had replied, looking up from some paperwork that had barely managed to capture her entire attention. But even as she'd asked, she had known. Checking over the day's roster that morning, his name had leapt from the page as if printed in huge, flaming letters that had burned into her brain and distracted her from the morning's work ever since.

She also didn't need to re-check the roster to know that 'He. . .who?' was now closeted with Yvonne the podiatrist, who. . .

'Lucky Yvonne—she'll actually get to *touch*,' Diane gushed, apparently reading Saunders' mind and adding her assumption that—despite her query—Saunders knew exactly who and what she was talking about.

'Oh, for goodness' sake, Diane. He's only a man, after all,' Saunders snapped. And added, 'He isn't some film star, or whatever; I don't know what you're so frothy about.'

Then, having admitted that she didn't need to be told 'He. . .who?', and having startled herself with the admission, she snapped her jaw shut and glared at her associate while wishing that she, herself, would some day learn to keep her mouth shut.

Then she had to grin. How long had it been, after all, since the centre had drawn a client of such undeniable attractiveness? The grin evolved to a hearty chuckle as she recalled the hulking, muscular blond surfie who had drawn a similar reaction from Diane last year, until she'd grown tired of explaining to him that an insulin-dependent diabetic simply could *not* survive on junk food and beer!

She found herself wondering—but definitely not asking!—about Diane's assessment of Fordon Landell's dietary habits. They would be, she thought to herself, simple and yet sophisticated, perhaps even contrary, like the man himself.

Then she pondered briefly if he, like most newly diagnosed diabetics she'd encountered, had some particular, special, favourite dish that would turn out to be forbidden in his unchosen but unavoidable new lifestyle. With Diane's ravings floating half-heard around her, she pored through visions of Fordon Landell devouring waffles drowned in maple syrup—her own downfall—gigantic ice-cream sundaes, handfuls of exotic peppermint-cream chocolates. Then, unbidden, came the mental image she had received after pricking his finger, when he had sucked away the final drop of blood with that mischievous, little-boy look in his eye. Memory of that brought a shiver that Saunders was glad Diane didn't notice.

'. . .take up podiatry; there's nothing romantic about *food*.'

Diane's voice finally won out, but only because Saunders' sense of humour was tickled by the ridiculousness of what she was hearing. All the old platitudes linking romance and food poured into her head, followed by an almost identical complaint—in reverse—that she'd heard Yvonne utter not six weeks earlier.

'There's not a lot of romance in feet either, unless you're a fetishist,' she replied, perhaps too sharply. She was remembering, and trying not to, just how her own pulse had raced in the simple process of taking Fordon Landell's blood pressure. 'And now, if you're through gushing, I have a client due.'

That client had taken up her time well past the end of Fordon Landell's session with the podiatrist, but Saunders hadn't been able to resist, during the final moments of the interview, wondering if he might have found some excuse to wait for her.

He hadn't, and she had been annoyed with herself for presuming that he might, then even more so at finding she was wishing he *had*.

And now you're going to a party you won't enjoy, probably overflowing with people you'll enjoy even less, just on the off-chance that he might be there? You want your head read, my girl, she thought as she reached the front door and paused to compose herself before ringing the bell.

Ignoring entirely the rather battered trench-coat—it lived in her car, mostly, and served, as tonight, a totally utilitarian role—the lightweight woollen dress, as sweeping in its line as in its multi-coloured, swirling pattern, was neither new nor classically fashionable, but it suited her colouring and, because of its sweeping lines, tended to obscure how much *too* slender she had let herself become.

The matching shoes had withstood the two-block hike without damage, and her tights had also survived. A miracle, she thought, given her usual luck. Of course, the wind had frothed her already rowdy hair into disarray, but a moment in the powder-room would fix that, or at least fix it as much as mattered.

I'll never make a fashion-plate, she thought, frowning slightly, and then switching the frown for a smile as the door opened to reveal Gail Mahoney, resplendent in a gown Saunders expected she had made herself, but which looked astonishingly expensive.

'Welcome, stranger. It's been too, too long,' was the greeting she received, and Saunders had to agree. It *had* been too long. The doctor and his wife were among her favourite people, and if she were more of a social animal. . .

'My fault,' she replied. 'I can't even plead overwork, as I'm sure Peter could. Just. . .well. . .'

A finely-drawn eyebrow was raised as Gail helped relieve Saunders of the ancient raincoat. 'You can't plead overeating as an excuse either, I see.' The doctor's wife shook her bright blonde head, frowning as she did. 'Honestly, Saunders. . .anorexia at your age? You're taking slenderness to an extreme, and I'm not just being envious when I say that.'

Gail Mahoney was frankly pudgy, might even have been called dumpy, except that her vivid personality made any such description a wasted exercise. She was. . .just herself, and so comfortable with that persona that Saunders knew envy was the last thing on her mind.

'I'm in top form,' she replied. 'Never felt better in my life.'

Then their conversation was interrupted by new arrivals, and Saunders found herself moving through a dense crowd of people, a glasss of wine in one hand, as she twisted and squirmed her way to a less crowded area of the large house.

There were some people there she knew; greetings assailed her from various sides as she smiled and nodded her way through the pack. But although she tried her best to survey the crowd without being *too* obvious about it, she saw no sign of Fordon Landell.

Serves you right, she was thinking a few moments later, attempting to shrug off a mingled feeling of disappointment and self-consciousness as she tried to follow the conversation of a prominent anaesthetist she knew only vaguely and liked less.

And then. . .

He *was* there. Saunders couldn't see him, certainly wasn't about to turn around to look, but suddenly she *knew* Fordon Landell was there, knew that he knew *she* was there, that he was deliberately looking at her, touching her with his eyes, consciously trying to make her aware of his presence.

And succeeding!

He couldn't have succeeded better if he'd dropped an ice-cube down the back of her dress, and indeed the sensation was spookily similar. She could feel little tendrils of. . .something. . .clawing their way up her spine on icy feet.

The words of the anaesthetist fogged around her, as vague and hollow-sounding as if they came from some great distance. She smiled politely, nodded politely when it seemed appropriate, and comprehended none of it.

It wasn't fair, she was thinking. Nobody should be able to have that effect on a person. Spooked, she took the first opportunity to ease out of the conversation, never turning round, fighting to keep her composure as she drifted away, moving slowly but surely to get the bulk of the crowd between herself and. . .

Too late.

'You're trying to avoid me, and I wonder why?'

The voice was low, husky, and too, too close to her left ear. But not a surprise; she had felt his presence, had somehow known he was moving through the crowded room with her, moving deliberately to counter her escape bid.

'Why, Mr. . . Landell, isn't it?' She turned to face him, forcing surprise into her voice, into her expression, knowing even as she did so that she was fooling neither of them.

'I certainly hope so,' he replied cheerfully, throwing her a shamelessly cheeky grin. 'Unless, of course, you've been trying to avoid somebody else entirely?'

'Are you all right?' she countered, retreating into boldness to try and cover the sudden fluttering in her tummy as she met the intensity of those black, black eyes. 'I mean. . .you've only got diabetes—not a persecution complex as well?'

Which gained her only a moment's respite and a quizzical glance with it. Then, a soft-spoken but definite warning. 'Neither of which would be an acceptable subject for public announcement, if you don't mind.'

The intensity of the remark made her look again at his eyes, and she also caught. . .something, in his posture, in the slightly off-balance way he seemed to be holding himself.

'You *are* all right?' And now her concern was genuine. Because he wasn't; Saunders was certain of that.

Her glance wavered from his too-bright eyes, dropped to the glass in his hand, flashed round the room evaluating the typical party savouries, returned to find Landell's eyes still fixed upon her, but no answer forthcoming.

She looked down at his glass again; not a wine-glass. Whisky? It would, she thought, suit the man.

'How long since you've had a proper meal?' she demanded, sliding into her nurse persona without breaking stride in her thoughts. His too-casual shrug was reply enough.

'Even money says you've had your evening tablet but you didn't eat tea,' she insisted, mentally kicking herself but quite unable to stop now. '*And* you've had a glass or two—I know Peter's idea of hospitality.'

'What *are* you on about?' He spoke now, but there was an edge to his voice, a firm, almost stroppy stubbornness.

Saunders thought wildly, almost angrily, He mightn't even have had *lunch*, for all she knew. And now the alcohol was aiding the pills in driving down blood sugar levels quicker than he was probably used to.

'Have you eaten anything *proper* in the last little while?' she asked, ignoring the increasingly stubborn gleam in his eye. She knew intellectually that she was handling this all wrong, knew that if he really *was* becoming hypoglycaemic she was more likely just fuelling his stubbornness, making him less likely either to admit it or do anything about it.

She looked up to find his black eyes fixed on her, heard him growl, 'If I didn't know better, I'd swear you'd just swapped that rather spiffy dress for your uniform. Don't you *ever* give it a rest?'

'You really ought to eat something,' she replied, keeping her voice calm as she looked swiftly around for some type of finger-food that had a bit of substance to it. If she was right, and she was becoming increasingly certain that she was, Fordon Landell needed some quick boost of sugar, that would bring him right and do it quickly. But then he would need something substantial, something high in carbohydrates, that would keep him from lapsing into another hypo all over again.

'What are you saying—that I'm drunk or something?' And the slightly belligerent tones made her all the more certain.

'No, I'm just wondering if——' She broke off, turned swiftly away as her eye caught sight of a tray of chocolates on a nearby side-table. She dashed over and grabbed two of them, returning to find Landell staring owlishly at her, shaking his head.

'Here,' she said firmly, 'get these into you.'

'Are you daft, woman? I can't eat *those*. Hell. . . you ought to know that.'

'Just do it.'

'No.'

'Please.'

'No.' And now he was getting decidedly stubborn; Saunders was sure of her ground now, if totally unsure of how to force the food into this infuriating man without causing a scene.

She paused, drawing a deep, steadying breath. Diabetics going into a hypoglycaemic state—even those who had suffered the problem before and were totally aware of the consequences—could be amazingly unpredictable, seeming to deny the problem with a mulish stubbornness if the process had gone too far.

'Well, *I'm* going to. What are you—afraid?'

She had the first chocolate almost at her lips before it was snatched from her grasp in a gesture so quick it surprised her. If he *was* having a hypo, it certainly hadn't affected his reflexes.

'The hell you are. Not until you explain to me in words of one syllable just what the devil you're up to.'

'You're having a hypo, or starting to. You have to——'

'The hell I am!' Decidedly stroppy now.

'And you're being repetitive.' Saunders was trying to be patient, knew she *had* to be patient, but. . .

'I'll give you repetitive,' he growled. 'Is that what this is all about—you think I'm having a. . .a. . . whatever?'

'Well, you are!' Except that she was no longer quite so certain; in fact, she was no longer certain at all.

'Am I? Or am I, perhaps, getting just a little bit. . .

tiddly?' he replied, with an almost sinister insistence. 'More than tiddly, even? Maybe fair-dinkum, three sheets to the wind——'

'I am not even *suggesting* you might be drunk! Just that. . . Well, you seem to me to be acting a bit. . .'

'Strange? My goodness, Nurse,' he countered in a voice alive with sarcasm. 'How truly, amazingly observant of you.'

And his black, black eyes mocked her now, laughing at her but laughing without real humour. Saunders had to force herself to meet his eyes, could manage that, but couldn't get her tongue round any suitable words of reply.

'Maybe I only get. . .strange. . .in *your* presence?' he continued, eyes still laughing but now with top lip curled in what she could only interpret as a sneer of satisfaction at having got beneath her guard. He didn't give her a chance to interrupt.

'Maybe——' and his voice slid into soft tones of deliberate seduction '—maybe I just get drunk on your eyes?'

Whereupon he laughed at what Saunders was certain must be the quite startled expression on her own face. But now, at least, the laughter was genuine, and after a moment's uncertainty she couldn't help but join in.

'I think you're in danger of believing our own bulldust,' she replied finally. And then, more seriously, 'But are you quite sure you're feeling all right? A moment ago you honestly did seem just a bit off. . .off-balance or something.'

'Not surprising,' he replied.'If this wasn't quite so public a place I could show you the bruises that account for it. I fell off a dirty great cliff the other day and I'm still just a bit stiff, that's all. Although——'

and he was kind enough to dilute his grin just a tad '—
I do have to admit that I actually *have* had quite
enough to drink, and it is about time I got some
"proper" tucker into me. You may not believe it, but
your rather charming dietitian did make a good bit of
sense during her part of my reconstruction process.'

Then he grinned again and continued. 'Just wish I
could say the same about the podiatrist; I don't think
I'd dare let her lay hands on me in my present
condition.'

Saunders nodded sagely, suddenly quite relaxed
with this weird man, but not sure exactly why. 'I'd
have thought you'd enjoy Yvonne's ministrations,' she
said. 'Most men do, I'm told.'

He shrugged, somehow making the gesture more
than it seemed. 'I'm more partial to a proper massage
than to clammy hands round my ankles,' he replied.
'Especially *cold* clammy hands—you ought to speak to
her about that.' Then he shrugged again. 'Still, she did
say I've got excellent pulses. Is that a virtue, I
wonder?'

And in the face of his wondrous expression of
innocence, Saunders could only grin.

'It suggests, as I'm sure you know, that you're not
having any great circulation problems in your feet,'
she replied. 'Yet!'

'There seem to be an awful lot of "yets" and
"maybes" involved in this. . .condition we share,
Nurse White.'

And there was something there, not so much in his
words but in his tone, and perhaps in the depths of
those damned black eyes, that told Saunders he was
saying a great deal more than the mere words con-
veyed. But what?

Best avoided, she thought. This man was far too deep, too complicated. His blatant flirting she could laugh at, perhaps even share, but when he started getting subtle. . .

Their mobile conversation had drifted them into the thick of the cocktail party and she suddenly realised she was gradually being pressed closer and closer to him; they might almost have been dancing.

And, as if picking her brains, reading her thoughts, he reached out to her, the half-grin on his wonderfully mobile mouth the only warning she got.

Her right hand automatically moved to meet his gesture, only to halt mid-way as she caught the unholy glee in his eyes and, for the first time, felt the stickiness as she started to open her fist.

Fordon Landell shook his head soberly, but the laughter flowed from him as he reached up with his other hand—this one waving a handkerchief—to pluck the remains of the second chocolate, now a sticky, congealed mess, from her grasp.

'Just so you don't go wiping it on your dress or anything,' he said with a chuckle, producing the first chocolate, the one he'd snatched from her only moments. . .hours. . .earlier, unsullied and wrapping it into the handkerchief with the mess of the other, then trapping her wrist in an iron grasp while he scrubbed away at the film of chocolate on her fingers.

'You're a *grot*, Nurse White,' he grinned. 'A proper little grot! I'll bet when you were a child you ran around in mud puddles and fell out of trees and came home with smudges on your nose.'

He reached out with the handkerchief in a playful swipe at Saunders' nose that would have had her rearing back in surprise if she'd had room to do so. As it was, she could only stare at him, no longer worried about him being hypoglycaemic, more wondering if he was actually sane!

Even more so when he tucked the handkerchief into the side pocket of his expensive, exquisitely-tailored sports jacket without apparent regard for the potential consequences.

'Evidence,' he said. 'I shall produce this for mine host when I complain about you on the way out.'

He glanced quickly to ensure his own hands were clean, then reached out to put the cupped fingers on each of her shoulders.

'Can you twirl?'

'Can I what?'

'Twirl,' he insisted, lifting one hand away only long enough to spin it in an unmistakable gesture before returning it to her shoulder.

Frowning, totally confused by this point, Saunders shook her head at the ludicrous suggestion, then accepted the pressure of his fingers and did as he requested.

'Right,' he said when their eyes met once again. He flicked his hands in yet another gesture that hardly required explanation. 'There goes your uniform; you are officially, definitely, *totally* off duty now, and I forbid you to so much as *mention* diabetes, illness, hospitals, or anything else of that depressing nature. I propose to take you out of this den of iniquity and go find some "proper" tucker. Agreed?'

Saunders met his gaze, a curious mixture of seriousness and frivolity, with a grin, finding herself both amused and entranced by it all.

'Agreed,' she said with a nod.

'Good,' he said. Then cast an approving eye over

her, making the journey a deliberately slow, leisurely one that took in every detail of her clothing and the body wearing it. His dark eyes were hooded, but the intention was clear enough, and Saunders thrilled to the implicit flattery.

'You'll do,' he finally said, meeting her eyes again with an expression she simply could *not* interpret with any accuracy. 'But—dare I say it?—you'll have to eat better than I suspect you usually do, or my friends at this place we're going to will be mightily put out!'

And before she could reply he had gripped her above one elbow and was expertly swivelling his way through the crowded room. Within moments, they had said farewell to their hostess, waved a goodbye to Peter Mahoney from across the room, collected Saunders' coat, somehow disposed of the chocolate-filled handkerchief and Saunders was being handed into the passenger seat of Fordon Landell's station wagon.

He waved away her suggestion that she take her car too, so as to avoid having to come back for it.

'We're not going that far, and besides, I'll have an excuse, then, to stretch the evening a bit further,' he said with a cheeky grin. Saunders didn't dare to mention that she was habitually early to bed, and that a long, long evening in his mercurial company might send her own blood sugar levels into orbit.

His chosen restaurant wasn't, it turned out, all that far away, and, from the reception they got upon entering, it seemed clear that Fordon Landell was a cherished customer of long standing. He was greeted as an old friend; Saunders was also greeted, not so subtly examined, and—it seemed—approved before they'd been guided through to a private table near the rear of the small establishment.

The blackboard menu listed a wide range of appealing pasta offerings, but Fordon Landell gave Saunders no chance to worry about making difficult choices.

'Just bring us whatever's best tonight,' he told their waiter, who had already arrived with a bottle of wine that was obviously his usual choice.

And here he observed etiquette, by asking Saunders if she approved, a gesture that was, she thought, largely wasted; she seldom drank, and wouldn't have known one wine from another, although she discreetly avoided mentioning that by merely nodding her acceptance.

His faith in the chef brought a grin from the waiter and, some time later, a gigantic divided platter displaying an intricately prepared variety of pastas and accompanying sauces.

'Where are the other six people you invited?' she had to ask, staring in partial disbelief, her nostrils singing with the tantalising aromas but her mind blocked by the sheer volume.

'Wait until you get into this,' was the reply. 'Besides, you need feeding up a bit; I know you have to be careful of your weight, but there *are* limits.'

'I am exactly the same weight I have been since I was. . . Well. . .I've been just this size for a long time,' she replied, unsure if his remark was a compliment or a complaint.

'And I've been exactly this weight, give or take a kilo or two, since I was eighteen years old, but when I told that to a certain dietitian not so long ago, in a certain unmentionable clinic where I was discussing a certain unmentionable. . .condition, she had the audacity to tell me I was ten kilos overweight—and logically, therefore, had been so virtually all of my adult life!' he replied. 'Can you imagine such a cheek? I very nearly slapped her down and sat on her.'

Which would have been the highlight of Diane's year, Saunders thought, attempting to stifle a giggle at the thought of Fordon Landell sitting on top of the diminutive dietitian. But she didn't tell him that.

Her thoughts grew increasingly personal as she watched him manipulating his cutlery with an expertise she couldn't begin to match. It was the same type of dexterity she had so often observed from top surgeons, many of whom, she knew, could construct the most delicate of joinings with nearly-invisible threads but could barely manage to tie their own neckties.

This brought another hidden smile as she applied similar logic to Fordon Landell while desperately trying to emulate his skill with noodles that defied her at every twist and turn.

'There's a trick to it, you know' he said, grinning as if he recognised and enjoyed the ability almost to read her mind. And, to her surprise, he rose from his seat and moved around behind her, reaching down to take her hands in his own, guiding her fingers so that spoon and fork were properly positioned.

But the effort, however well meant, was wasted. Saunders was too aware of him, of the warmth of his body against her shoulders, the firm strength of his fingers on her own, the sheer, almost overpowering prescence of him that seemed to flow into a cloak around her.

Instead of learning, her fingers trembled, fumbling the cutlery as a combination of embarrassment and uncertainty overwhelmed her.

'For goodness' sake, people are watching,' she hissed, trying in vain to free her fingers and managing only to tumble pasta all over the table. 'I'm not a child, after all.'

'No, I can see that,' he replied, removing his hands only to let them slide up her arms, to—incredibly—poise them on her shoulders, touching, caressing. The voice that had been so calmly directing now changed, took on a softer, more subtle tone as his fingers worked some strange magic.

And then, as suddenly, it was over, and Saunders felt strangely disappointed as he left her to return to his own seat, where he sat observing with a slightly raised eyebrow as she struggled to regain her poise.

'No,' he said musingly, almost as if speaking more to himself than to Saunders. 'No, you're not a child.' Then the focus changed as his eyes darted from the messy tablecloth to Saunders herself. 'But, as I seem to recall saying earlier, my dear, you're very definitely a *grot*!'

'It's your fault,' she replied. 'I was doing just fine until you. . .you. . .'

Her objection sputtered into laughter then, spurred by his own infectious grin.

'Just as well,' he said, when both had subsided into a sort of cautious watching brief. 'You'll enjoy your meal much more now that you can quit worrying about being neat and tidy. Relax, Saunders; that's the point of the exercise, after all.'

Relax? How can I relax when you've only got to touch me and I go all strange inside? Those and similar thoughts scurried through Saunders' mind, but if Fordon Landell was able to read them, he kept it well-concealed and busied himself with the meal.

Saunders did likewise, and found, ridiculous as it seemed, that her meal *did* become more pleasurable now that she could cease trying to be tidy and just enjoy. And, as the meal progressed, she found herself enjoying more, relaxing even further.

By the time for coffee, they were *both* comfortable, she decided. On a first-name basis finally, although 'Ford' rolled precariously off her lips and she privately wondered if he was having the same trouble with her name.

He had explained how he'd been named for a Tasmanian property where his adoptive father had once worked; she had told him how her mother, upon finding that she would only ever have the one child, and that a girl, had insisted upon the use of her own family surname as a first name for the infant.

'I like it,' he had said. 'It's. . .different—and I don't mean "different" in the way the word is so often used. But Saunders suits you, somehow. Although I suppose it ought to after. . .how many years?'

'Thirty-three, if you absolutely insist upon knowing,' she had replied. 'And I'm only telling you that to be fair, since I have your file to inform me of. . . Well. . .'

'Anything else you want to know, just ask me and I'll tell you,' he'd said with a grin. 'I don't have any secrets, except the one you know about and about which I now remind you. I know this sounds strange as hell, but please, just follow my lead, would you?'

His eyes had flickered away from Saunders for a moment, towards the entryway, she thought. Now they clearly indicated that someone was approaching, and Saunders had only time to nod her understanding—she hoped!—of his strange request, as he rose to greet a woman whose stunning, sultry beauty was almost enough to disguise the cloud of icy anger that surrounded her.

CHAPTER FIVE

COLD. That was Saunders' first and overriding impression of the woman. Cold, and almost brittle in that coldness.

But beautiful with it. Tall, almost as tall as Ford himself—and *this* woman's slenderness could never be criticised; her fine bone-structure carried an elegant voluptuousness, vibrated with a studied, sensuous sexuality.

A mane of rich, dark mahogany hair, perfectly coiffured, classically beautiful features, a long, slender neck. . . And eyes that now did their best to rip Saunders into digestible pieces as her low, throaty voice concentrated on Ford Landell.

'Darling. . .you promised to meet me at the Mahoneys' little do,' she said, voice registering a calm that her entire attitude denied. She moved in against Ford, clearly expecting to be kissed, and Saunders was inordinately pleased to see her escort comply without any particularly obvious enthusiasm.

'If I hadn't decided to come this way and noticed your car. . .' The woman paused dramatically, perhaps, Saunders thought, realising how revealing her statement had actually been, then shrugged and continued, 'Well, I wouldn't have known *where* you'd got to, would I?'

'I promised I'd get to the Mahoneys' if I could, and, although it may not look that way, I did,' Ford replied, not specifically contradicting her, but Saunders detected a certain bite to his voice, and was certain the other woman had also caught it.

Then he was introducing her to Nadine Fitzmaurice, who hardly acknowledged the introduction except to throw Saunders a 'who the hell are you? look before continuing her interrogation.

'But if you were there, and you *knew* I was coming. . .' she said, icicles dripping from every word, then had to let it go; to continue the question would only serve to provide answers she obviously didn't want to hear, didn't want to know about.

Saunders remained silent. This, she thought, was definitely *not* her business. But it was, unquestionably, entertaining in its own peculiar way. Obviously Ford had started this evening with one date and ended it—no, had got this far—with another. What other surprises, she wondered?

'But you know Peter's bashes,' he was saying now. 'Noisy, overcrowded with boring medical types, not enough room to change your mind, much less discuss anything remotely like business. . .'

'Business?' Nadine Fitzmaurice's voice echoed the question in Saunders' mind. Her attitude indicated that she didn't believe the explanation, and the dark-haired woman fixed Saunders with a frigid stare that *dared* Saunders to explain.

Not on your life, Saunders thought, returning the stare with her most professional smile and then turning *that* on Ford Landell. This is *your* story, little mate; I'm going to let *you* carry the can, she thought, but said nothing, and knew from his expression, somehow, that he didn't expect her to.

During the long silence that followed she wondered if he was just going to drop it there and hope the exquisite Nadine would accept that. Which she would *not*, Saunders surmised. But, after silently pulling over an extra chair and seating both women, then signalling for fresh coffee, Ford leapt back into the fray with what could only be called *élan*.

'Sugar,' he said without preamble. 'I've taken an interest in sugar recently, and Saunders has a good deal of expertise in the subject. . .mostly on the management side.'

Whereupon said expert only *just* managed to avoid biting her tongue as she choked back a hysterical giggle. The absolute *cheek*! She found herself looking from Ford Landell to his elegant. . .girlfriend. . .not daring to speak, hardly daring even to meet their eyes. Especially those black, black eyes that now danced with a sort of unholy glee.

The rotter! He was *enjoying* this, actually revelling in it!

Nadine Fitzmaurice was not. She, too, was glancing from Ford to the other woman in the party, and it didn't take any of Saunders' professional empathy to figure out what the woman was thinking.

But on the surface. . . Ice, Saunders thought. The woman is as chilly and brittle as the inside of a deep-freeze.

'Nadine's interests are more in the mining area,' Ford was saying, and if he noticed that woman's chilly response to the entire conversation, he was careful not to show it. 'Her father is one of my——'

'Employers,' said Nadine, and shot Saunders a look that might have been described as triumphant.

'Clients,' said Ford, continuing as if Nadine hadn't spoken at all. 'He has interests in all sorts of minerals all round the country, but he isn't into sugar—or, at least, I don't think so.'

The glance he directed towards Nadine Fitzmaurice urged her to pick up that bait, but she was too busy glaring at Saunders to notice.

'Actually, sugar is only one of my. . .interests; I'm a nurse by profession,' said Saunders, throwing the comment out to whoever might bite, smiling to herself as she caught just that glimmer of reaction from Fordon Landell, who apparently had thought for at least an instant that she was about to blow his perform-ance right out of the water.

But on the periphery of her thoughts was the intriguing contradiction of terminology—employer or client?—and the proprietary tone so evident in Nadine Fitzmaurice's voice.

Ford's comment that her father had no interest in sugar had not seemed, on the surface, to hold any particular further warning to Saunders about not revealing his diabetes. It might only have been meant to indicate on his own behalf that he had concerns in which the woman's father was neither employer nor client.

Whichever, she determined then and there to let him carry this verbal time-bomb all by himself; she would not reveal his diabetes—could not, with any professional ethics—but she was damned if she was going to let him lead her into. . .whatever!

The arrival of their coffee, somewhat to her delight, merely served to complicate the situation. She already knew he liked his coffee sweet and white—he'd had to borrow her sugar substitute tablets for the round of coffee they'd had before Nadine's entrance.

Let's see you get out of this one, she thought,

leaning back in her chair and pointedly directing her gaze at the sugar bowl that seemed, suddenly, to dominate the centre of the table. Ford could, of course, simply use sugar; it wouldn't hurt him at all that much. But somehow Saunders knew he would not—it would be, she thought, a loss of face he would not accept without a fight.

Nor did he, but his approach caught her quite by surprise.

He simply waited until Nadine reached into her designer handbag—as he had known she would—and brought out *her* sugar substitute pills, then, with a brief but clearly triumphant glance at Saunders, borrowed them. Nadine's reaction—or, more correctly, lack of reaction—made it only too obvious that it wasn't the first time he'd done so either.

His point made, Ford then went on to dominate the limited conversation with deliberate small talk, keeping to 'safe' subjects, drawing upon his considerable skills as a raconteur to keep the conversation moving, until he could truthfully announce, 'We honestly must go, Nadine. It's getting on for pumpkin-time, and I must return Saunders to her vehicle. Probably silly to have left it at the Mahoneys' in the first place, but there you go. Do you want to follow me out, and we'll see if the party's settled down to something civilised, or. . .?'

No fool this girl, Saunders thought, as the Fitzmaurice woman countered that offer with one of her own, an offer that didn't surprise Saunders and didn't surprise Ford Landell all that much either, judging from his response.

'It's too late to party,' Nadine replied with a warm smile that did not include Saunders. 'Perhaps I'll just go home and prepare the nightcap I promised you, so that when your "business" is over, it will be ready.'

'Why don't I just grab a cab back?' Saunders asked, both relishing and hating the slightly trapped expression Ford couldn't quite hide. 'It isn't a problem for me, really, and I don't want to be the cause of upsetting your plans in any way.'

'Nonsense. I wouldn't hear of it,' was the stern reply, and his eyes flashed an even stronger message as he quickly rose from the chair.

'Really,' she insisted, 'it's no trouble. I've taken quite enough of your time this evening. In fact——' and the words were out almost faster than she thought of them '—if it's all the same to you, I might just walk back; it isn't far, after all.'

'Too damned far to walk in this weather and at this time of night,' he replied, Nadine almost ignored now in the deliberate matching of wills.

Careful, my lad, this one isn't going to appreciate being ignored, and I doubt she'll put up with it either, Saunders thought, but couldn't help herself continuing to stir.

'You're absolutely sure?' she asked, hiding the inner grin as his jaw firmed in ill-disguised frustration.

'I am *quite* sure,' he replied, and before she had another chance to speak his fingers were digging into her elbow as he took her arm and practically dragged her from the restaurant. Indeed, they were two doors down the street, Nadine Fitzmaurice trailing behind, before the startled waiter could catch up, the account for the evening's meal held out with obvious trepidation.

Ford Landell's muttered 'Damn!' was followed by a quick apology, but there was no apology in the glare he fired at Saunders as he followed the waiter back inside, reaching for his wallet in the process.

Right, she thought with strange satisfaction, and turned quickly to the other woman, who seemed either confused, amused or both by this element of the situation.

'I really feel like a walk,' Saunders said, with a shrug and a nod of her head towards the restaurant. 'I'm sure Mr Landell won't mind, not really; he's just trying to be courteous.'

And without waiting for a reply, not sure if she could expect one and not caring either, she turned on her heel and strode off.

It was, she admitted as she walked along, a decision open to charges of petulance. 'To which I would happily admit guilt, because I *am* being petulant, but I'm also damned if I'm going to put up with any more of this nonsense,' she said aloud.

And some minutes later, in a much louder, much firmer voice, she replied, 'No, I am *not* out of my mind,' when Ford's vehicle pulled up beside her and she was asked the question in a voice that boomed like thunder.

'You could have fooled me,' he said. 'Now, stop this nonsense and get in, if you don't mind.'

'But I *do* mind,' she replied, looking him in the eye and then turning her head away as she continued her march.

He tried humour, then.

'You're making my blood sugar go all frothy; I hope you realise that.' This through an open window as he drove along beside her.

'You're too cold-blooded for it to be a problem,' she snapped, stepping up her pace and looking for the right opportunity to cross to the other side of the street.

'And *you* are being deliberately. . .frustrating,' he snapped, expertly manoeuvring the big station wagon to thwart her intention. 'Now, please, Saunders, be sensible.'

'Diet and exercise,' she reminded him. 'That's sensible, and that's the principle I'm following. I ate far, far too much of that delightful dinner, and now I'm having to compensate for it. You ought to try something similar—preferably in *that* direction!' And she pointed behind her, shaking her finger like an outraged schoolmistress, aware of the comparison, and too frothy herself even to care.

'I'd get even better exercise taking you over my knee. . . Hey, stop that, dammit!' he said, as she turned quickly and darted across the empty street behind his vehicle before he could stop her.

Should have done this in the first place, she thought. Now it was clear that he couldn't follow along beside her, but must stay on the other side of the road or find himself going in the wrong direction.

Her satisfaction lasted only moments; a block ahead, Ford had parked the four-wheel-drive and was stalking across to wait for her on her chosen side of the street, moving with a deceptively casual smoothness, almost arrogance.

Saunders paused, half inclined now to turn and flee, to retrace her steps, anything to avoid the confrontation she had set herself up for but no longer really wanted.

Ford made no move to approach her; they stood there, eyes locked in a contest of wills, but too far apart to speak or be heard.

'Go away,' Saunders whispered, not really knowing why she bothered. 'Just go back to the party, or to your nightcap, or to hell, for all I care, but go. . .and leave me alone.'

Wasted effort; he couldn't hear her, probably wouldn't comply if he could. His only move had been to lean up against a lamp-post, arms folded across his chest as he waited, comfortable, confident.

'No!' She spoke aloud, but knowingly to herself this time. 'No!'

She turned abruptly, walked away with long, deliberate strides. A few metres behind her was the entrance to a small neighbourhood park that cut across to the next street in a dark, tree-lined tunnel.

No sane place for a woman at this time of night, she thought, and an instant later was there, her high heels stabbing into the turf, making her clumsy, increasing her feeling of vulnerability. Behind her, the sound of her name was an invisible shadow, easy to ignore.

The residential street ahead was dimly, poorly lit, compared to the thoroughfare she had just left. And the small park was even worse; distant streetlights used the larger trees to draw faint, wispy shadow figures, but the ground along the high fences at each side loomed black and menacing.

From the pool of darkness ahead and to one side came a faint rustle of noise, then a more distinct one — a clink of glass against glass that seemed to cry its own warning. Saunders paused, common sense starting to assert itself as she began to realise the stupidity of her situation, the potential dangers.

She halted, eyes searching the darkness, while her mind churned with serious misgivings. One thing, she thought, to score points off Fordon Landell. But this, this was. . .

'Madness!' she whispered, unaware she had even spoken until the reply came from just behind her.

'Madness, for sure. Now, don't panic, Saunders; it's only me.'

The voice was calm, steadying; the fingers which reached out to take her hand, to turn her into the welcome protection of his arm, seemed strangely gentle and reassuring.

As he turned her, Saunders was astonished to realise she had only moved a half-dozen steps into the park, which from the relative safety of his grasp seemed no longer so threatening, but no longer a haven either.

'Are you right out of your tree?'

The gentleness was still there, but it was different now, the edges ragged like the edges of his voice as he steered her back to the footpath.

'My God, woman, surely you're not *that* angry with me?' he said, then continued speaking as he marched her straight across the street and turned towards his parked vehicle. 'Damn it, Saunders. What have I done to get you *this* fired up?'

Touched me, she thought, half wanting to pull free of his grip on her elbow, half wanting to lean into him, to feel the strength of him, the reassurance she knew was there. Touched me, she thought again. That's all you did and it isn't fair. But when she spoke, guilt combined with her earlier, unreasoned, illogical jealousy to make her waspish, irritable.

'You have nothing to do with. . .with any of this,' she snapped. 'You aren't even supposed to be here; you have a date for a nightcap, unless you've forgotten.'

'Ah. . .' Fingers that had seemed to be clamped on her elbow as if welded there now slackened, although he continued to guide her gently, keeping her with him as they approached the vehicle.

But that was all he said, and the resultant silence fuelled her guilt, brought her inner turmoil to boiling point. She had been a fool to enter that darkened park, perhaps had been a fool to set off by herself in the first place, but. . .

'I fail to see that it's any of your business that I decided to walk back and get my car,' she said, forcing herself to stop now so that she pull free of his grip.

'I am not in the habit of taking girls for dinner and then letting them walk home or. . .wherever,' he replied calmly, reaching out to open the vehicle's door as they paused before it. 'And I'm not about to start now. In, please.'

'I would prefer to walk; really, I would,' she insisted, more for the principle than the fact. The incident at the park was quite insignificant, but it had spooked her just a little, however much she tried to deny it to herself.

'In.'

No room to argue now; black eyes glared into her own and one hand pointed to the vehicle's interior while the other coiled loosely around her waist, effectively preventing any escape.

Saunders obeyed, reluctantly, only too aware of his hand at her elbow as he assisted her up into the passenger seat, even more aware of how quickly he moved around to his own side, sliding into the driver's seat with a fluid, cat-like movement, fingers flying to insert the key in the ignition, then to a nearby switch. She heard the snick of the door beside her locking.

'Now,' he said, and now his voice was ragged, but no longer quite so gentle, quite so calm. There was the throb of anger there now, anger and. . .something else she couldn't decipher, but knew, instinctively, she wasn't going to appreciate.

'Now?'

She kept her own voice soft, neutral, trying to cover her uncertainty and knowing from the look in those dark eyes that she wasn't managing very well.

'Yes, Nurse White. . .now!' he said, his eyes unreadable, but shining, she thought, with unholy glee. One strong hand reached over to pick up her fingers, which he examined as if they were something rare, unusual, valuable.

His touch was half caress, half some other sort of gesture, but Saunders couldn't figure out just what. All she knew was that her pulse raced because of it, then raced even faster when he lifted his eyes and began using them to caress her face, her mouth, her entire *being*, without saying another word.

'I would like it clearly understood that I do not take a girl for dinner and then leave her to find her own way home, regardless of. . .unexpected interruptions,' he finally said, softly, quietly, almost musingly, as if he was really talking to himself, not her. 'But that isn't the point; the point is why you felt this strong a gesture was really necessary.'

And now his eyes were definitely glinting, reaching out to capture her gaze, forcing a response, demanding it.

'I think you're making far too much of this,' Saunders replied calmly, denying the racing blood that throbbed at her temples, trying to ignore the way his fingers now traced intricate little designs along her wrist.

'Am I?' His grin was slow, deliberate. 'I suppose now you'll say that you'd planned to walk back anyway, that Nadine's arrival had nothing to do with it.'

'If I'd known you already had a date, I wouldn't have gone for dinner with you in the first place,' she replied, deliberately ignoring the fact that getting some 'proper' food had been mostly her idea. 'If Miss. . . whatever-her-name-is was upset by it, I'm not surprised; I'd be upset too if I had made plans to meet you and then found you'd wandered off with some other girl.'

And you're starting to sound and act like a lovesick, jealous teenager, she thought. You've got no claim here and you don't even want one; there's nothing here for you.

'If I didn't know better, I'd think you might be showing just the teensiest bit of the old green-eyed monster,' he said, and his eyes laughed as his fingers moved along her forearm, their touch a tantalising, dangerously seductive message.

'You. . .you. . .conceited. . .arrogant. . .insufferable. . .' Saunders could only stammer helplessly at the audacity of it. She yanked her arm away from his fingers, those fingers whose touch had been so seductive only a moment ago, but now. . .now. . .

Ford Landell looked down at his hand, looked at her, turned his hand over and looked at it again, his entire expression one of surprise and amusement, then of mock indignation—the look of a little boy caught with his hand in the cookie jar.

'You're a funny girl,' he said, shaking his head and

then deliberately, primly, folding his hands in his lap.
But there was nothing prim about the look in his eyes;
he was laughing at her and no mistake about that!

'Fine,' she said, after a moment of trying to dominate him with her glare and failing miserably. 'So I'm
funny. Well, when you're finished laughing, Mr Irresistible Landell, perhaps you'd like to drive me back
to my car so that I can go home and be funny in peace.
Or at least have the decency to let me out of here so
that I can *walk* back, as I originally intended.'

His gust of laughter was unexpected, but nothing
compared to his reply.

'If you're going to insist on acting like a lovesick,
jealous teenager,' he said, and Saunders flinched
inwardly at his use of her own thoughts against her,
'you have to expect to be laughed at. I mean, really,
Nurse,' he continued, shaking his head in mock
sorrow, 'it's all right to get in a royal snit and walk out
on somebody, I guess, but the whole thing loses a lot
of impact when you start walking in the wrong
direction!'

And as she stared at him, horrified at the realisation
that he was undeniably, embarrassingly, humiliatingly
right, he laughed again, then leaned over and kissed
her.

It started off, she had the remaining sense to realise,
as a friendly, even a sharing kiss, the type she might
have expected had Ford been laughing *with* her instead
of at her. But, as their lips met, something happened.
Ford's lips touched hers, gently searching her mouth for
a response, then moved away again, only to be replaced
by fingers almost as feather-soft, almost as searching.

Saunders felt his thumb on one side of her mouth,
his fingers on the other, looked up to see those black,

black eyes only inches away, felt his left arm move, lift, drop back to encircle her shoulders as he turned her to meet another kiss.

And this kiss was different! As their mouths united, she found herself leaning into the kiss, savouring the taste of his breath, the texture of his tongue as it probed the softness of her lips. She heard his voice sighing, felt his breath go all ragged as her own became even more so, felt warm tendrils of sensation that seemed to flow from his lips to her own, then down along the inside of her, until they formed a starburst somewhere about her middle.

His fingers had left her cheek now, were moving along the line of her neck, probing at the neckline of the dress, flitting along the soft swell of her breasts. His lips followed, leaving behind a haunting moan, then only the memory of that as he kissed her along the joining of her collarbones, his lips moving hungrily, his tongue following, then leading as her own breath soared into a moan of her own.

When his hand touched at her breast, lifting, cupping, caressing, she knew his mouth must follow, knew she wanted that, was already thrusting herself against the pressure of his lips, the warmth of his breath, as he kissed, explored, touched.

Her right hand was trapped between them; her left was no longer in the command of her brain. She was aware of it moving along the muscular line of his shoulder, felt the harsh texture of his coarse hair against her fingers. And as he shifted imperceptibly in his seat the trapped hand scrambled for its freedom, wandering unguided along the strength of his thigh, feeling the warmth of him through the knife-edge crease of his trousers.

She felt his breath catch at her touch, both felt and heard the sigh that whispered against her lips.

Now her dress was off her shoulders, her breasts exposed fully to his touch, to his kisses, to the delights of his tongue flicking her nipples to an almost painful stiffening.

'I want you,' he whispered.'Oh. . .lord, how I want you.'

Saunders could not reply; his mouth moved to capture her own before she had any chance to think of the right words, even to assume there could *be* any right words. She knew that her needs matched his, her desire matched his, but there were no words to answer him; only her body could do that.

And it did! When his fingers roamed down the front of her, playing a tune along her rib-cage, teasing the flat planes of her tummy, her body arched against the pressures. When his fingers roamed beneath the looseness of her skirt, whispering along the fabric of her tights, her muscles drummed to a tune of their own, tightening to hold his hand *just* there, flexing loose to speed his journey, guide him.

Then they reached their destination, only to be halted by the barrier of the tights—was that his moan of disappointment or hers? Whose was the voice in her head that raged at him to rip away the barrier, to touch her, possess her, reach the very core of her being?

Whose voice——? No, *voices*, she realised with surprise a moment or a lifetime later! Saunders opened her eyes as she was suddenly released from Ford's arms. The appearance of a group of strolling teenagers across the street, too far away to see her disarray, yet certainly near enough to comprehend the situation—

their cheery shouts of approval proved that!—had shattered the intimacy of the moment as if it were glass.

Ford's mood changed in the instant, and although Saunders sensed immediately that his anger was more in her defence, more at her potential embarrassment than anything else, the swiftness of the change was daunting.

'No!' Her objection sprang from lips that still tingled from his kisses, from a mind that still spun from the ecstasy of his caresses but now recoiled from the grim expression in eyes that an instant before had been soft with. . . She didn't care with what—she only wanted now to forestall the violence she could see erupting. Even the youths must have sensed it; their voices changed, the postures became defensive, and they moved on as Ford's hand reached for the door-handle.

'No!' she said again, daring to reach out, to grip at his other arm, pulling him round to face her. The bleakness of his eyes now was frightening, even to her, but to her surprise it faded even as he looked at her.

'Please. . .'

'Of course,' he replied, and his fingers flew to the ignition, his feet to the proper pedals.

They drove in silence through the forever it took to reach Saunders' car. Ford Landell kept his eyes on the road ahead, his expression rigid. Only the faint pulsing of his jaw muscles as he fought back his anger and frustration revealed how tense he was inside. Saunders busied herself in straightening her clothing; she felt shamed, disorientated, confused. Words tumbled through her mind, emotions tumbled with even less order through her entire being, but she said nothing, *could* say nothing.

'I'm sorry for that; it was my fault,' he said when they finally parked on the street behind her car.

Saunders didn't reply. She was already yanking at the door-handle, angry now at the humiliation, frustrated by the fact that the door on her side was still locked, by the fact that her fingers shook so badly, that her entire body was trembling.

Caught necking in the car like a couple of teenagers? she was thinking, and shivered visibly. *His* fault? She silently cursed the body that had betrayed her, the body that still held the imprint of his touch, of his caresses. Her lips felt puffy, would *be* puffy, she knew, and her knees were trembling so badly she wondered if she would be able to walk when she did get out.

'I. . .' A hand reached out to touch lightly at her cheek, ignoring how she flinched away. Black, black eyes glistened, drinking her in. 'My God, but you're lovely.'

The words were a whisper, softer even than his touch. Then he laughed, and it was a growl of laughter, coloured bitter and black as his eyes.

'Caught necking like a couple of kids,' he said, and the words emerged in a sort of chuckle that held black, bitter humour.

Necking? She had thought that, but deep inside she knew it had been far more than that. Had they been somewhere else, had the situation been different, the circumstances different, necking would have been the least concern.

'I. . .I have to go,' she finally managed to say. She didn't want to discuss this, didn't want to think about it, even to remember it, although she knew she would always do that. 'Now, please.'

'Shall I follow you home, see that you're. . .all right?'

'Why?' Her voice had shrilled; she could feel it, knew he could hear it. 'Why? So you can have another kick at the cat?'

'Saunders. . .really. . .'

'Let me *out*!'

He started to speak again; she cut him off. Abruptly. Angrily. Vicious in her choice of words, her tone of voice.

'You have somewhere else to go, I seem to remember,' she sneered, feeling triumphant for whatever reason as she heard the snick of the lock releasing beside her, felt the door-handle move in her fingers.

'I hope you enjoy your. . .your nightcap; you ought to be just about warmed up for it,' she snapped, and was out of the door, slamming it behind her against the sound of his reply.

'Damn the nightcap!'

He was out of his own door, striding ahead to grip her arm as she leaned down to search with her key for the lock. His fingers were like a steel clamp, lifting her, turning her to face him.

'I want to see you again, Saunders,' he said. 'This thing isn't going to stop here; I won't let it, I——'

'You *what*? Let me go!'

She raged against his grip, tore free, reached again to insert the key. This time his fingers flashed down to snatch the keys from her fingers; she turned to find him holding them high out of reach.

'Give me those!'

'Not until you settle down. You're not fit to drive when you're this upset.'

'I'll give you upset! Damn you. . .give me my keys!'

'Are you going to listen to me?' His voice now was calm, too much so. His eyes had a look she couldn't interpret, didn't dare to!

'You have nothing to say that I'm interested in hearing,' she replied angrily. 'Now, will you please just give me my keys? It's late and I would like to go home. . .by myself!'

'When am I going to see you again?'

'Try *never*.'

Ford shook his head, half sadly and, she suspected, half in jest.

'You can't mean that. There was too much between us back there just to. . .toss it all away.'

'There was nothing between us you couldn't arrange just as easily by giving me my damned keys and going off to your. . .your date,' she insisted, reaching up in a gesture that she knew was futile before she made it.

'I don't *have* a date,' he roared, stretching higher, looming over her now. 'Get that straight, Saunders White. I do not have a date! I had an understanding. . .a. . .a. . .'

'Look,' she said, returning his glare, 'I don't care if you call it a date, an understanding, or a flying pink pig. Just give me my keys and get on with it, whatever it is!'

'The only date I had, actually, was with you,' he replied in a voice strangely soft, unexpectedly calm after his earlier outburst.

And then, even more surprisingly, he acquiesced. 'Have it your way, then,' he said, handing her the keys with a shrug. 'Drive carefully, Saunders,' he added, eyes now totally unreadable but strangely sad-looking. 'You're much too pretty to waste.'

CHAPTER SIX

SAUNDERS stared into the mirror, hardly able to recognise the naked woman with the mad tangle of wind-blown hair and puffy, wounded eyes that returned her gaze with astonishing calmness.

Behind her on the bathroom floor was her clothing, discarded in an untidy mess. Especially the party dress she'd hastily stripped from her body and flung away as if it had somehow betrayed her. Never, she thought, ever to be worn again.

She looked in silence at the over-slim figure before her, abstractedly noting the contours, the seemingly swollen breasts that somehow managed to keep tingling, as if reaching out for more of Ford Landell's caresses.

But in her mind thought became voices, voices became images. She flinched inwardly at those, and at the memories—'Caught necking like a couple of kids'. Her thoughts, his words. . .or was it the other way round? Did it matter? It was true—that was surely enough.

The voices, the faces of the youths, floated through memory, no longer quite as humiliating, as degrading as they had seemed at the time.

'I probably ought to thank them,' she told the mirror girl, who didn't seem in the least disturbed by the evening's performance. *She* had an almost smug look, the puffy eyes redolent with some vague expression of self-satisfaction, of mysterious, hidden pleasure. *She* would have been just as pleased if the teenagers hadn't

interrupted at all, would have enjoyed continuing to
share Ford's lovemaking; *she* probably would have
roped and tied him and dragged him home with her.

Saunders looked as hands lifted the reflected
breasts, **as** fingers smoothed a path down a flat stomach
that rippled in memory of a different touch, different
fingers. The image grinned at her through lips that
must still tingle as her own did, shrugged shoulders *he*
had touched, had caressed, had explored with his lips
and fingers.

Is it so long, then, since a man looked at you that
way, made mad, passionate love to you, treated you
like a woman? the image seemed to say, the words
hollow, mocking, the voice somehow trembling, as did
her own knees. Even worse the trembling inside her;
her stomach felt hollow and empty, fluttery, and the
fluttery feeling dipped lower, touching the core of her
as gently as had his fingers.

So long? No man had *ever* made her feel quite like
this, Saunders thought to herself. No man had ever
even tried, much less with the heady success Ford
Landell had managed.

'We'll just ignore the fact that nobody before ever
had such overwhelming help from *you*,' she muttered
to the image in the mirror. 'You've become dangerously wicked and wanton in your dotage, my girl.'

Wanton. It was, she decided as she snuggled into
her pillow, a deliciously descriptive word. But a very
dangerous condition! The night's adventure, she told
herself, must be taken as a serious warning; she must
at all costs keep Ford Landell at a healthy arm's
length, or suffer the consequences. Because she'd been
hearing from him again, seeing him again—there was
no doubt of that in her mind. Nor was there any real

doubt that she wanted to hear from him again, although preferably at a time and place of her own choosing, and in circumstances a good deal safer than those just experienced.

Among her last thoughts as she finally drifted into sleep was the questionable blessing that he didn't know where she lived and her telephone number was not listed, so she ought to be safe from his attentions until Monday morning, at least.

Strange, then, that one of her first thoughts upon waking was to wonder if Ford had returned to the party or gone on to his scheduled rendezvous with the stunning Nadine Fitzmaurice. Not, Saunders determined resolutely, that she was particularly interested, much less—as he had so graphically described it—green-eyed jealous.

She specifically said so to the creature in the mirror, who looked no better than the night before as she manoeuvred it into a tracksuit and forced it through a brutal exercise programme aimed at dissipating memory, seeking a return to physical and mental equilibrium. She felt considerably revitalised as she finally settled down to a breakfast of muesli and wholegrain toast.

The problem was, she found, as the day, then the weekend progressed, that her rejuvenation was more physical than mental. By Saturday night she was thinking, for the umpteenth time, that Ford could easily have got her number from the Mahoneys, could easily have telephoned, *should* have telephoned. Should, she decided firmly by Sunday noon, have attempted *some* gesture of reconciliation, or. . . well. . .something!

By Sunday night she had decided she didn't care

anyway, and Monday at work was spent snarling and snapping at everyone silly enough to get within reach, although she insisted to herself that Fordon Landell had nothing whatsoever to do with her foul temper.

You're a fool!

Ford had told himself that as he watched Saunders drive away, then found himself repeating the exercise as he started his own vehicle and did the same. He was still repeating the accusation in a kind of distracted litany when he arrived at his own home, mysteriously having bypassed both the party and Nadine's flat in the process.

This realisation left him staring at the telephone, almost angry at having let himself be manipulated into having to make a phone call he didn't want to make, having to find excuses he didn't want to find—or manufacture.

'Something I ate—either at the party or later, I don't know which, but whatever it was, it's playing havoc with my insides,' he was saying a few moments later, uttering the words without conviction and really not caring if Nadine believed him or not. Likely she didn't, but he wasn't concerned with that. He merely wanted to get the duty over with so that he could concentrate his thoughts on Saunders White.

'And I'm expecting a very early call that might have me on the road before daylight, so I'd best grab what sleep I can,' he continued. Not quite a lie, although the call was more likely to come on Sunday night or early Monday morning. But it served.

Then he found himself prowling through his home, moving abstractedly, haphazardly about the place, seeing it almost from a stranger's perspective as he wondered how Saunders would react to it. He was tired, but not sleepy, unable to dispel from his mind the events of the evening.

He boiled the jug for coffee, then found himself sitting at the kitchen table with a glass of red wine in his hand instead, and his mind filled with visions of flashing, passionate blue eyes. Having then remembered to do his bedtime blood test, he had to do it twice, because the first time he missed the time-count, distracted by tactile thoughts of Saunders, of how she had felt in his arms, the texture of her soft breasts beneath his fingers, of how her lips had moulded themselves to meet his kiss.

He woke several times during a restless, troubled sleep, certain he could detect the scent of her on his pillow, once even convinced she was there beside him, snuggled into his arms just as his erotic fancies stipulated.

There was no pre-dawn telephone call in the morning, but he was up before the birds anyway, still restless, still moody and tense. An hour's bicycle ride—carefully navigated to avoid the implausible risk of encountering Nadine—left him physically more settled but mentally as confounded as ever.

He simply could not remember being so singularly attracted to any woman, with neither rhyme nor reason, sense nor logic. Especially considering that he wanted children eventually—lots of them. And *that* was something he hadn't actively considered until he'd found out about his diabetes, and about her diabetes! The hereditary consequences worried him, but even more bothersome were the risks he now knew to be involved for any diabetic woman contemplating having children. Millions of them did so, of course, but. . .

His mind ranged through the risks, trying dispassionately to find a clear path of thought, but it kept switching tack on him, returning to the night before and the woman he'd held in his arms, made love to, wanted, needed. . .

But to have resorted to such juvenile tactics as he had last night, necking in a car, on a public street, was. . .laughable, but somehow not quite funny. Not really. How long had it been since a woman had attracted him sufficiently for him to make such a complete and utter fool of himself? Memory, thankfully, failed him.

But you ought to have given up that kind of foolishness years ago, he told himself, then idly wondered why, considering how much he had enjoyed it. Then wondered less idly how Saunders was reacting in the cold grey light of dawn. She had responded to him, no question about that, but then, when they had been so rudely interrupted. . .

About the only saving grace was being able to laugh, now, at his fiery reaction to the cheering youths the night before. With the questionable benefit of hindsight, he could only be thankful for Saunders' restraining influence.

'They'd have ended up playing soccer with your head, mate, and serve you right,' he muttered to himself, then laughed again, half wishing he could meet that same group of ruffians this morning.

He cycled past a telephone box, paused long enough to realise he didn't know her number, rode another half-block before turning back to make a futile investigation of the bedraggled telephone book, then realised he had no change or telephone card with him anyway, and hadn't the slightest idea of where she lived, or with whom.

That thought touched off a little mental landslide of speculation that occupied another kilometre or so. Did she live alone? Share, as many women did? Live at home? No, she had mentioned that her parents were dead. Or did she have, for instance a *male* flatmate? It wasn't uncommon, but what bothered him most was the visceral discomfort he got just from the idea.

Was he going to see her again? Too right, he was! But except for doing so professionally, where he rather presumed she had little choice, would she want to see *him* again?

He cycled past a florist, not yet open, then halted outside a confectionery shop, and was eyeing a wondrous display of boxed chocolates when the sheer ludicrousness of that idea struck him.

Send chocolates to a girl who can't eat them? You've really lost the plot, boy. He chuckled to himself. Ten more kilometres for penance, and then you want your brain checked—not just your blood!

He was well down the road when it also occurred to him that this shop, also, wasn't going to be open for two hours more at the very least.

Home again, he found himself prowling as restlessly as the night before, and at one point was halfway through dialling the Mahoneys' number when he glanced at the clock and stopped one digit short of making himself unpopular with them as well as Saunders—people who survived late-night parties hardly being expected to appreciate telephone calls before breakfast.

The confectioner still wasn't open when he drove past, *en route* to the office and an attempt on some distasteful but necessary paperwork, but Ford rewarded his foolish earlier impulse with a shake of his head and a wry grin.

His work was continuously distracted and interrupted by random thoughts about what suitable gesture he might come up with to redeem himself for last night's performance, but to little effect. He was inordinately pleased to be rescued by an unexpected phone call that sent him rushing to the airport; by mid-afternoon he was many metres underground, his attention so focused on the problems before him that even erotic thoughts of Saunders couldn't intrude. At least not until that evening, and the next, and the next. . .

The week dragged for Saunders; her work, her lifestyle, all seemed normal, yet somehow her time sense had become warped. And, throughout, there was this strange perception that the very normality of everything was what was wrong.

She kept finding herself mentally drifting, her mind returning at the oddest times to the events of Friday night, to her own feelings and responses, to textural memories of Ford Landell's kisses, his caresses. At work it was simply distracting; at home, in the unexpectedly lonely hours of late evening, these memories were distinctly disturbing. And in the dark hours, when she found herself waking without apparent reason, her skin tingling, her nipples turgid with the desire his touch had created, the memories were torture.

You're mad, or getting that way, she thought. He doesn't phone, he doesn't write, or. . .or anything! And why should he, after all? Certainly you made it clear enough that you didn't want him to.

She was able to keep from thinking too often or too clearly about how Friday night might have ended, but less able to keep from speculating about how it had ended—for him! Had he returned to the party, or gone on to his rendezvous with Nadine? She thought that logically he must have, but some small voice inside her kept telling her different. The voice of hope, or just wishful thinking? she wondered. If so, it was a voice to be rejected, a voice she ought not listen to. And yet. . .

She kept on hearing *his* voice, hearing the distinctness of specific things he'd said, and the way he'd said them.

'I want to see you again, Saunders,' he'd said. 'This thing isn't going to stop here; I won't let it. . .'

'There was too much between us back there just to. . .toss it all away.'

And, 'You're much too pretty to waste.'

There had been something. . .something unique in his voice when he'd said that. Something, she kept thinking, quite different from the lust-induced rhetoric of his earlier statements.

'*Are* you going to waste?' she asked herself aloud at one point. And, having thought about it, decided to defer, ignore, avoid any detailed, honest answer. All she did know was that, until Ford Landell had stepped into her existence, she had been generally content and at peace—now she was confused, no longer sure of her place in the scheme of things.

How could he make such statements as he had? How could he touch her, reach out to her, and then simply disappear without a word? How could he kiss her the way he had, somehow reach inside and turn her inside-out? 'How could I let him?' she wondered aloud.

It distracted her the most that next Friday, made the drive home a hazard to everyone else on the road, and did absolutely nothing to prepare her for arriving home to find him sitting on the front steps, waiting for her.

'You're not to roust on poor old Peter; I threatened him with physical dismemberment if he didn't give me your address and phone number,' Ford said as he rose, cat-quick, to open the car door and hand her out.

He was dressed casually in a plaid shirt with rolled up sleeves, moleskins and the expectable gleaming boots, and the effect was to make him look younger, somehow, and marginally fitter than when she'd seen him only a week before.

'I'm sure he was just terrified,' Saunders replied tartly, trying as she spoke to pull her hand free from the grip into which she had so unthinkingly placed it when he'd opened the car door.

Ford blithely ignored the taunt, equally ignoring the lack of subtlety in her reply. He didn't release her hand either.

'I would have called sooner, but I was away,' he said. 'And I didn't want to call you at work because I didn't—don't—know your policy about personal calls there.'

'I can just imagine you worrying yourself to death about that. Will you let *go*?' she retorted, again trying to yank free of his grasp, failing, then almost toppling backwards as he complied without warning. His fingers let go, but his eyes held her, she fancied, just enough to slow the momentum of her recoil.

Black, black eyes, eyes that seemed to see right into her, see past all her defences, while revealing nothing of the mind behind them, nothing of his reasoning, his logic, his true feelings. Eyes that said without speaking that he knew she was curious, but that he wasn't going to discuss it, much less explain it—not without being asked.

Well, not by me, she thought, determination firming her stance as she stood there, forcing herself to meet his gaze without flinching, without revealing how those eyes made her insides melt, how his touch had done so even more.

'Why are you here?' she finally managed to ask, and almost cried out with frustration as her voice—in her own ears—sounded flat, totally lacking in authority. Damn him! He didn't even have to speak to her to be in control. He just stood there, seducing her with his eyes, with his very attitude!

'What are you afraid of?' he countered, either ignoring her question or deliberately choosing to keep her on the defensive. 'Or do you just enjoy complicating everything? Obviously, I'm here because you're here; I came to see you, to talk to you.'

Then he grinned, as if he actually enjoyed the effect he was having on her. 'Did you think I just dropped by so we could stand here like a matched set of garden gnomes, staring at each other and exchanging stupid questions?'

Saunders just looked at him. The mental image he'd created made her want to laugh, but if she did that he would win. . .again! And she didn't want that, couldn't *have* that.

'What makes you think I want to talk to you?' she finally managed to reply. And her mind was thinking, What a stupid thing to say! Of course you want to talk to him, if only long enough for him to explain about

Friday night. Which he isn't going to do, not unless you ask. And you won't!

'But you have to,' he replied, voice soft now, deceptively so.

'I do not!'

'But you are.'

'Oh. . . This is childish,' she snapped.

He merely elevated one dark eyebrow and grinned at her, a tiny, almost smirking little grin that was followed by an eloquent shrug.

'We could always just stand here and watch the grass grow.'

'*You* can if you like; I have things to do.'

She lifted a foot, actually thought about stepping round him, just walking off and leaving him standing there. But the raised foot didn't move; her muscles somehow refused to obey her. Or else he actually *could* hold her immobile with a single glance!

'Name three,' he replied, without seeming to notice her movement. And his voice was a growling purr, his eyes laughing at her now. 'Apart from making us a coffee, which would go down rather well, I think.'

Saunders glared at him, hating him for his control, hating herself for her lack of it. But she didn't reply, somehow just couldn't make her mouth work around the words. Couldn't even think of any words!

'You have to wash your hair. You've got a heavy date. You're expecting company any minute,' he said, not bothering to hide the sarcasm. 'How's that? Come on, Saunders. . . You can't really still be shirty over what happened a week ago, surely?'

'I don't see why not,' she retorted, unsure whether to laugh or get angry. 'Did you expect me to have forgotten? You certainly haven't.'

'No,' he replied, and now his voice, his eyes, his entire demeanour had changed, somehow. There was a sudden alertness, as if the very air around them had suddenly become charged.

'No,' he repeated. 'I haven't, and I'm not likely to, and I'm glad you haven't, because you damned well shouldn't. But are we going to keep up this juvenile squabbling forever? We aren't teenagers, Saunders, regardless of how things. . .happened last Friday night. We're adults, and what we were feeling were very adult feelings that aren't just going to go away if we don't talk about them or if we just stand here like a couple of teenaged kids and try to deny their existence.'

'Aren't you making just a bit much of a little grope session?' Saunders snapped. Knowing he wasn't. . .or was. . .or she was. Damn him! he only had to look at her and she went weak at the knees, but she must keep him from being so sure of himself.

'I *have* been kissed before, you know' she added spitefully, then let real bitterness creep in. 'Although hopefully not just as the lead-up to a main event somewhere else.'

He should have had the grace to look embarrassed, or turn his damned black eyes away, or. . .or. . . something! But not Ford Landell. He just looked at her, raised one eyebrow, and then laughed!

It was the final straw. Saunders had no problem moving this time, and was halfway round him when one arm reached out to snag her, to draw her in against him, negating the wild swing of one hand aimed at his face.

'You are amazing, you really are,' he crowed. Then his mouth swooped down to capture her own, his arms locking her own by her sides, holding her too close against him for her to follow the temptation to lift her knee into his groin.

Saunders struggled, but in vain. His lips ground harshly against hers, then softened and began to manipulate her mouth even as she tried not to respond. Her wriggling served only to emphasise their closeness, to fan the waves of heat that leapt from his body to her own.

And then, as abruptly as it had begun, the embrace was ended. He set her down, well away from him, and with a wary eye on the leg she swung with vicious intent. There was laughter in his eyes, laughter—but caution too.

'I always seem to go too far too fast with you,' he said. 'You affect me in the most amazing ways, Saunders; it's uncanny. But let's get one thing straight—I did not go where you obviously think I went after we parted last Friday night. I went straight home to bed, to a very lonely bed, I might add, because you weren't in it and I wanted you to be.'

Answer that one, my girl, she told herself silently, thankful that at least her mind was working that much, because her tongue certainly wasn't. She couldn't reply, didn't dare. Didn't really even want to, because it was just too dangerous. Ford stood there, looking down into her eyes, everything about him shouting out at her that he was being literally truthful, that he simply meant what he'd just said.

'I. . .I wish you wouldn't talk like that,' she said after an aeon of silence.

'Why not? It's the truth. . . And you know it, what's more. Don't you want to know how I feel? Or is it your own feelings you're so afraid of?'

It was too much, too fast, too. . .everything. Saunders could only look back into his eyes, tongue-tied, suddenly terrified by the intensity of the discussion. She hardly knew this man, yet she had already almost succumbed to his sexual magnetism, knew she would again if she didn't break his control, knew she didn't really want to break it, knew. . .

'Well?'

'Well. . .what?' she replied, knowing how dumb that must sound, knowing exactly *what*, but simply incapable of allowing herself to respond.

'Well. . .which? Or is it both?' he asked, and there was a tinge of exasperation in his voice now, she thought. 'It isn't such a difficult question, Saunders.'

It is when I don't even know how I feel, she thought, but couldn't say that. Besides, she actually had a fair idea of her own feelings; that was half the problem. All of her training, all of her professional attitudes dictated against becoming involved, but she had started to do so anyway.

'It's unprofessional.'

The words were out even as she thought them, and uttered more to herself than to him. But they had an immediate impact; his eyes darkened, the intensity of his stare became almost overwhelming as he looked down at her.

'Of course,' he finally said, after what seemed an eternity. 'It's unprofessional. Now, why didn't I think of that?' And his voice had a curious flatness, as did his eyes.

'Of course,' he muttered, apparently speaking to himself, looking at her, through her, with eyes that might have been blind they were so expressionless, so utterly cold.

'Of course,' he said for a third time, 'you realise that is utter and total rubbish, Saunders. Or at least I hope you do, because if you don't, you've got yourself even more confused than you've got me. And that, Nurse, is very, very confused indeed!'

He folded powerful arms across his chest, then stood there in stubborn silence, running his eyes provocatively over Saunders from crown to toenails. And no longer were those eyes cold; even as she watched she could feel the heat of his gaze, could read the desire there, the naked, undisguised wanting. Just as he meant her to.

And all she could do was endure it, standing as if turned to stone, unable to speak, unable to fight back. And, worse, unable to control her body's reaction to this visual plundering.

It was as if he was physically caressing her, tuning her like some living musical instrument. His gaze touched at her throat and slid lightly down the hollow of her shoulder. Her tummy turned over, feeling hollow as his eyes moved lower; her hips seemed to flex as if ready to dance to whatever tune he might order, although her legs felt like limp springs, barely able to hold her upright.

She endured, at first, then found herself drawn into the amazing aura he seemed to be projecting around them. She found her awareness heightening, becoming tight as a drawn bow. Her peripheral vision seemed to be expanded; without taking her eyes from his, she was none the less conscious of the faint movement of his chest as he breathed, could almost focus individually on the curling hairs revealed by the open-necked shirt, could feel the strength of him, the sheer, masculine, physical presence.

She could see his breathing quicken, along with her own. Could *feel* it, just as surely as if her fingers were touching that muscular chest. They might have been alone on the face of the earth, although somehow she still knew that they were standing on the front lawn of her unit, in full view of her neighbours, of anyone driving down the street. And she knew, too, that he had only to reach out and touch her, or speak to her, and he could take her inside—as she wanted him to do—and finish the lovemaking he had started the week before.

And suddenly she knew that he wouldn't!

The perception came seemingly from nowhere. But it shattered the mood surrounding them as effectively as a scream.

She wanted him to. He knew it, had deliberately created that want in her, had done so without even touching her. And now?

Saunders closed her eyes momentarily, just long enough to be sure she had broken the spell. Then she opened them again in full expectation of seeing Ford Landell's face as he savoured his triumph, in full expectation of hearing him voice his rejection in the most humiliating terms.

CHAPTER SEVEN

SAUNDERS frowned as she listened to the message from Reception, but it was less the message than the implications involved that forced the frown.

Damn Ford Landell anyway, she thought. He was playing at something, but either it was too simple or too complicated for her to understand it totally.

This was the third time in a week that he'd cancelled out on his scheduled appointment with her. The first, following their traumatic parting on her front lawn, had seemed reasonable enough, but now she was beginning to twig that things weren't as simple as they might have seemed.

The second cancellation, also made through Reception and with quite reasonable notice, had offered no excuse—simply that he couldn't make it. But this time?

'I'm not sure what his problem is,' her receptionist had told her. 'Last time he cancelled he suggested he would be happy to see one of the other nurse-educators, but of course I said that if he'd begun with you he should probably continue. He didn't object, or anything, but. . .'

'And this time?'

'Well. . .' The receptionist clearly wanted to avoid this, but her tone of voice was enough to alert Saunders.

'Well?'

'This time he. . .well. . .sort of insisted, I'm afraid. I tried to convince him otherwise, of course, but he

104

seemed rather determined. And when I suggested he really ought to speak to you first, and said you were free just at the moment, well. . .'

'Let me guess. He suddenly pleaded an emergency and got off the phone?' Saunders suggested.

'Not exactly.' And now there was definite tones of alarm in the receptionist's voice. Saunders didn't know the woman's previous work-history all that well, but was beginning to think it must include some classic examples of the messenger being shot for delivering bad news.

'Well?' she enquired, and didn't bother to hide the tone of exasperation she could feel growing in her voice. 'Look, I'm not going to come out there and beat you with a big stick just because some client has said something. . .well. . .less than complimentary. What did he say, for goodness' sake?'

'Well, I didn't really understand it, to be honest,' replied the receptionist, who was unquestionably honest but occasionally not too awfully bright. 'He said there was an issue of conflict of interest involved, and he didn't want to be responsible for compromising your professional situation. Whatever that means. . .'

It means Mr Landell is being bloody-minded and extremely annoying, Saunders thought, but didn't say so in quite those words. She simply suggested he was a 'difficult person' and left it at that, at least as far as her receptionist was concerned.

'If he calls again, and I can only assume he will,' she said, 'then see if you can fit him in with one of the other girls.'

Then she sat staring at her crowded desk blotter, eyes not properly focusing on the masses of paperwork

before her, mind sliding back to her last encounter
with Ford, nearly two weeks ago now. . .

She had been right in her realisation that he wasn't
going to push the advantage he'd so deliberately
contrived. Rather than simply reach out and collect his
prize, simply reach out and take her into her own
home and make love to her in her own bed, he had
conjured up a wall between them.

It had been no more tangible than the way he'd
seduced her without touching her; she couldn't see it,
or touch it, but she knew it was there, had almost been
able to see him building it, brick by invisible brick. He
had done it with his eyes, with his body language, with
his entire bearing; it couldn't have been clearer if he'd
been using real bricks and genuine mortar.

And when it was done, he had looked at her through
those black, black, eyes, eyes bleak with some emotion
or lack of it that she couldn't quite define, and spoken
in a voice so dispassionate it had cut like a knife cast
from ice.

'I've sort of lost my taste for coffee after all,
Saunders, if you don't mind,' he'd said, obviously
choosing to overlook the fact that she had never
offered him coffee—that had been his own idea, all
along. 'I tend to look at it as a social drink; it doesn't
taste quite the same in a professional setting.'

And he'd shrugged, one edge of his mouth twisting
in what could have been either a sneer or a quite
disparaging grin.

'So we'll leave it, I guess. For now!'

And he had raised one eyebrow as he'd nodded that
curt farewell, then turned on his heel and walked
away. Before Saunders could even think of a reply, he
had been in his vehicle and driving off.

Reflecting upon it now, she was surprised at how calmly she had taken his departure, considering how easily he had just managed to get her all stirred up by just a phone call to her office.

'Well, I've got no time for this today,' she said aloud.

'There's too much involved in getting this promotion organised, and I daren't spare the time to worry about you and your strange little games, Mr Ford Landell.'

The promotion, which would take all of the following week, was in conjunction with a national diabetes awareness campaign, and would involve most of her staff setting up at a major regional shopping centre, where they would be offering free public glucose testing to all comers.

Saunders had done this sort of thing before; it was relatively simple, at least in concept, but when combined with trying to maintain the efforts of her office at the same time, the logistics sometimes became quite involved.

Which was exactly how it turned out. One of her nurse-educators took sick the first morning, several glucose monitoring machines that had been borrowed for the promotion failed to arrive on time, and the testing unit—for reasons never to be known—ended up at the exact opposite end of the shopping centre from where it was advertised to be.

By Tuesday morning, Saunders found herself abandoning the office to go and help out. By Wednesday morning she knew her own work at the office was going to have to be ignored for the rest of the week. By Thursday afternoon she'd had her foot run over by an erratic shopping trolley, had an ice-cream cone dumped in her lap and a glass of soft drink dumped all down the front of her, had been kicked in the shins by one of her far too many screaming brats, answered her millionth—with minor exaggeration—stupid question, turned up more than seventeen people who had had to be advised to seek further testing as suspected diabetics, and was thoroughly and totally fed up with the entire human race.

Whereupon Ford Landell showed up, Nadine Fitzmaurice clinging limpet-like to his arm, just to round out her day!

She had seen them perhaps an hour before, strolling, she had thought, with all the appearance of a long-married couple with time on their hands. Or tourists, perhaps. They had not seen her; she had made sure of that—she had thought!—by turning away and making a quick trip to the loo for whatever repairs could be made to her drink-stained appearance.

There hadn't been many—and now she was supremely conscious of how totally dishevelled she must look, especially when compared to Nadine's glossy, expensively dressed appearance. Ford was, as usual, in casual gear, but his boots gleamed and his trousers held a knife-edge crease that was almost as sharp as his eyes when he and Nadine paused before Saunders' station.

'Afternoon, Saunders. . .you look as if you're having a busy day,' Ford said, nodding graciously, courteously, and to Saunders' eyes quite impersonally. Nadine Fitzmaurice said nothing, but her eyes took in Saunders' appearance with a quite malicious pleasure.

Saunders hid behind the façade of her professional smile, but took a malicious pleasure of her own as she watched Nadine's eyes cruising over the various posters and advertising bumph, and saw the visible change as the dark-haired woman's comprehension altered.

It was like watching an old cartoon with light-bulb captions. She could almost *see* Nadine making the connection between Saunders' presence here and their first meeting, with Ford's—with hindsight—ridiculous comments about Saunders being involved in the management side of the sugar industry. It would, she thought, have been quite hilarious, except that Ford saw it too, and shot her a warning glare which she blithely ignored.

Instead, Saunders launched into her professional spiel about the various symptoms of diabetes, the value of such a service as this free testing service, and all the rest. None of it did a thing to relieve Nadine's curiosity, she noticed; throughout the spiel, Ford's companion kept shooting speculative glances, both at him and at Saunders herself.

But when it was suggested they partake of the free testing offer—'You're here, after all'—Nadine's attitude changed dramatically, and Saunders realised immediately that the other woman was almost terrified of submitting to the test procedure.

'It's all perfectly safe, I can assure you,' she said then, in her best professional manner. 'And it doesn't hurt a bit; I've been doing all sorts of children throughout the week without so much as a tear.'

Then she looked at Ford, and with sudden inspiration suggested that he might like to go first. His immediate glare told her what she wanted to know—he was suspicious that she might be setting him up somehow! He should realise, of course, that if he was keeping to his proper regimen, his blood sugar at this time of day should register quite within normal limits.

But he might forget that if he was at all flustered, and if he'd been playing up. . .

'Of course, although children are usually quite unafraid of the testing—it's only a pin-prick, after all—I have found that some grown men aren't quite so easy to deal with,' Saunders said—mostly to Nadine—as she guided Ford to a seat and began laying out the lancet device, testing strips and glucometer.

'You're not one of those pseudo-macho types who faint at the sight of their own blood, I hope?' she asked Ford, smiling sweetly and chortling inside at the scathing glance she received in reply. The problem with such stirring was that she knew—and he knew too—that she was at risk of her own hand trembling as she lifted his wrist and swabbed at the chosen finger with an alcohol wipe. She explained as she went along the need to ensure there was no contamination from sweet substances like jam or ice-cream, and was inordinately pleased to find her responses as steady as his own.

Nadine looked as if she was totally uninterested in the entire proceedings, and Saunders could sense that the other woman would never co-operate when it came to her turn to be tested. She couldn't help wondering if it was simply a reaction not at all that unusual, despite her professional denials, or if Nadine knew something that Saunders did not.

She kept up the professional patter as she pricked Ford's finger, milked out a single drop of blood and continued through the process of running it through the glucometer, safe, now, within her sphere of expertise, her fingers steadier than her heart—but of course only she could know that.

It was difficult not to laugh at his self-satisfied smirk

when the instrument registered his blood sugar at a comfortable five, especially when she could see, and both of them knew that there was a flickering concern behind his boldness that it might have turned out differently.

'There now; that wasn't so bad, was it?'

He shrugged. 'Not so long as you're quite satisfied, Nurse.'

And there was that damned unholy glee back in his eyes, Saunders saw. He'd drawn out that word 'satisfied' just enough to give her a message, without passing it on to an apparently still uninterested Nadine.

'Oh, quite,' Saunders replied, but didn't dare to try and meet his eyes solidly; she knew he would be laughing at her still, and not bothering to hide it that well.

Besides, her attention was already shifting to where Nadine Fitzmaurice stood, visibly nervous beyond all logic, shifting from one expensively shod foot to the other and looking round with eyes that, to Saunders, revealed the other woman to be on the verge of outright panic. In her peripheral vision, Saunders had noticed that Nadine had turned away, so as not to look when she had pricked Ford's finger, and had not turned back their way until the testing was clearly over. And, beneath the perfect make-up, that classic bone-structure was covered by skin as pale as chalk.

What to do? There was nobody else waiting, or she would have quietly suggested that Ms Fitzmaurice might forget about being tested. It would have been easy enough to laugh it off, specifying one test per couple, or something. Because Saunders was certain, without knowing the reasons, that Nadine could not and *should* not be forced to endure the test procedure she so clearly feared.

She turned to meet Ford's imperative black eyes, and was just slightly startled to realise that he, too, had caught the by-play, and even more so to see that he totally agreed with her feelings. He didn't say a word, but it was all there in the imploring glance he shot her. Thankfully, there was no need for the issue to be carried any further; a totally unexpected arrival saw to that!

'Saunders White, you're as gorgeous as ever,' said a new voice, and Saunders turned with undisguised pleasure at the sound.

'Simon! But I didn't expect you until tomorrow,'she cried, and moved quickly forward to the embrace offered her by Simon Connelly, one of her oldest and dearest friends and the featured speaker at Friday night's special public lecture on diabetes.

'When a ravishing creature like you offers a man bed and breakfast, she oughtn't to expect him to limit himself to just one night,' he replied, tightening his embrace and kissing her provocatively on the mouth before releasing her and holding her away.

'You're too thin,' he said then. 'I suppose you've got some fella running you ragged, and I'll have to find someplace else to stay after all.'

'Certainly not!' she replied, forcing herself not to look in Ford's direction, even though she could *feel* him mentally trying to influence her answer. 'I've been so looking forward to this visit that even if there was somebody else, I'd boot him out in the street just to make room for you.' And make what you like of *that*, Fordon Landell, she thought.

'You're sure?' And did she imagine it, or had he

glanced just briefly in Ford's direction? Certainly
Simon Connelly was more than capable of picking up
the strong vibes that must be in the air; he was one of
the most perceptive men she'd ever met. He held an
equivalent position to her own, but in a vastly larger
clinic in Sydney, and was considered one of the
country's foremost diabetes educators.

Simon was just her own age, and above average
height, with reddish-blond hair and classic good looks
that allowed him to moonlight as an actor and
occasional model so successfully that he enjoyed both
a dual salary situation and a lifestyle that many men
would envy.

Without appearing to look, she saw Nadine subtly
tugging at Ford's sleeve, noticed his move away with
her, and was certain there was a hint of reluctance in
his movements. Nadine, she thought, had simply lost
interest, was taking this heaven-sent opportunity to get
away from the scene; she wasn't so sure about Ford.

'I'm absolutely positive!' she replied to Simon, and
had the questionable satisfaction of seeing Ford's jaw
clench, felt the black glare he shot at her before
turning away into the shopping crowds.

Simon was sitting in her lounge-room when Ford
telephone that evening. His presence there was her
personal contribution to helping keep down the costs
of his visit to address Friday night's public meeting,
with the added enjoyment of Simon's company. They
had known each other since high school, and had
remained close friends at varying distances over the
years. When she went to Launceston in a few weeks'
time, on a similar mission, she expected to be billeted
rather than put the local diabetic group to the costs of

a hotel room. On this occasion, however, Simon had been able to go one step further, by arranging a modelling assignment that weekend which would pay for his travel costs as well.

'I'm calling to offer you dinner and a show tomorrow night, if you're free,' Ford said, his voice calmly casual. Too casual, Saunders thought, and wondered.

'Not possible, I'm afraid,' she replied. 'I have a. . . a house-guest, and I'm committed anyway, to the diabetes lecture tomorrow night.'

'Yes, of course; I'd. . .forgotten about that,' was the reply, saying far more by its inflexion and Ford's tone of voice than by the words themselves. The trouble was, she thought, she could not decipher exactly *what* she was being told. Ford had known about the lecture; he could hardly not have, considering how it had been advertised. She had even mentioned it to him, she was certain, during their ill-fated dinner after the Mahoneys' party.

The remainder of their conversation was first stilted, and then, Saunders felt, downright uncomfortable. Ford was coldly if politely correct in every word, but something in his voice made it perfectly clear to her that he didn't much like the situation. Her own side of the conversation was made even more difficult by Simon's frank and undisguised interest.

'Well, Saunders,' he said, when she had finally ended the dialogue and hung up. 'Sounds to me like you weren't being quite truthful when I twitted you about our accommodation arrangements this afternoon. Not surprising; I suppose that rugged-looking type who was hovering there has something to do with all this? The one with the silver hair and the absolutely ravishing dark-haired woman hanging on to him like grim death?'

Saunders tried to brazen it out, but without much confidence. 'How on earth could you put together a wild theory like that?' she asked. 'Not the business about there being a man; there is—sort of. But for you just to pick one out of a thousand others at a major shopping complex——'

'Was dead-set easy, given my years of experience in such matters,' Simon finished, with a laugh. 'Or a guess very easily confirmed by your face, my dear. You ought never to try and dissemble, much less attempt any outright lying; you're as transparent as window-glass and your. . .friend isn't much better, I have to say. If looks could kill I'd have been dead on the floor the instant I mentioned staying with you.'

He paused, then continued, 'None of which surprises me all that much, although his lady-friend was, I thought, surprisingly blind to almost all of it.'

'His lady-friend is terrified of the sight of blood, I reckon,' Saunders said, then thought about it a bit more. 'No, there's more to it than that, but just what's involved, I'm not all sure.'

This redirection bought her a few moments of precious time, but all too soon she was faced with Simon's wry grin and the question she had known must come.

'This is pretty serious stuff, I gather. You want to talk about it?'

'It isn't serious; it isn't *anything*,' she protested. 'And no, I don't want to talk about it.'

'All right,' Simon agreed. And steered the conversation in some other direction for some time before asking, 'So, what's his name?'

Saunders, only belatedly realising that she hadn't been paying the slightest attention, and that Simon both knew and had encouraged that, told him.

'This sounds even more serious than I thought,' he said some hours later, yawning as he made his way to the guest-room. 'I'll have to look this chap over a bit more thoroughly at the meeting tomorrow night. . . Or is it tonight, now?'

'Tomorrow night, if only just,' Saunders replied. 'But what makes you so sure he's going to attend the meeting? He hasn't mentioned it, obviously hadn't even considered it, or he wouldn't have phoned to ask me out.'

'Oh, he'll be there,' her friend assured her. 'I practically guarantee it. Although I wonder, frankly, if the poor lad has any idea what he's getting into. A girl as truly naïve as you, dear Saunders, is ten thousand times more dangerous than the gorgeous creature he was with today.'

'You're *such* a flatterer, Simon,' Saunders replied, kissing her friend goodnight on the cheek. She was inside, safe in the privacy of her own bedroom, before she admitted to the silent mirror that Simon's final remark might be correct, but it was still very, very worrying.

It was small consolation, after another long day at the shopping centre—a day made only marginally easier due to Simon's assistance, because yet another of her own staff had succumbed to the flu—for Saunders to find that Simon had also been correct about Ford attending the lecture, although she found it a bit of a surprise, for reasons she couldn't quite explain, to find him accompanied by Nadine Fitzmaurice.

Considering her certainty that Ford had wanted to conceal his diabetes from Nadine that night in the restaurant, and that the fact that he had given away every indication of feeling the same way— or so she had interpreted it—at the shopping centre clinic, Saunders found herself wondering how he had explained to Nadine his interest in attending this particular lecture.

But the real surprise was saved for later, after the lecture was over, when Ford and his companion came over to where Saunders was quietly congratulating Simon on its success.

'Most impressively done,' Ford said, reaching out to shake Simon's hand, then greeting Saunders and waiting just expectantly enough so that introductions must be performed. And from there it was a carefully stage-managed step on Ford's part to invite Simon and Saunders to join himself and Nadine for a drink.

'I . . . Uhm. . .' she stammered, in a bid to circumvent this situation, only to find herself betrayed by Simon's interest.

'What a splendid idea,' he interrupted. 'We'd love to, of course. Although,' he added, shooting a significant glance at Saunders, 'we'll not be wanting to make a long session of it; I've only a limited time here, and we do want to make the most of it.'

'Of course,' Ford agreed, but Saunders didn't miss the flicker of some strong emotion that had passed lightning-quick across his black eyes. Still, he was politeness itself as he directed them to a nearby lounge that was plush enough to be comfortable and quiet enough that they could converse without having to shout.

Ford organised drinks for them all, then gently

launched into a battle of wits between himself and Simon that would have been hilarious, Saunders thought, had she not been the meat in the sandwich. Ford was clearly trying to elicit from Simon the reality of his relationship with her, while Simon countered by seeking to establish—at least in his own mind—the reality of Ford's relationship with her.

Of course Ford was at a supreme disadvantage, being unaware that Simon already knew who he was and where he fitted in the scheme of things. And unaware, too, that Simon was leading him along a track that was very crooked indeed and fairly stinking with red herrings.

The duel was conducted by some complicated masculine set of rules that Saunders couldn't begin to understand, although it quickly became clear enough that both men did. What also became quickly obvious was that the performance seemed designed to keep Simon amused, Ford frustrated, herself fascinated, confused and repelled, and Nadine Fitzmaurice—apparently—merely bored.

With his astute understanding of human nature and his fore-knowledge of Saunders' relationship with Ford, Simon set out deliberately to torment both of them. Without ever getting specific, without ever giving Ford, in particular, anything tangible to work with, he drew them through a maze of discussion that implied intimacies that did not exist in his relationship with Saunders, meanwhile drawing from both of them their attitudes towards marriage, children, relationships—the lot!

Saunders thought she would never survive the two men's exchange of views about how hypothetical people entering a hypothetical relationship might consider such hereditary aspects as diabetes. She almost died when Simon brought up the subject, then found herself being drawn into it against her will. It was made no easier by Simon, ogling her like a schoolboy in lust, and Ford also shooting glances at her that were far less easy to interpret.

The performance lasted through just two rounds of drinks, no more than an hour in actual time, but to Saunders it was an eternity. She felt as if she was being torn to shreds by the two men, both mentally and emotionally. Simon, she realised, was merely playing games—allegedly with her own best interests at heart. But Ford Landell—very definitely—was not!

CHAPTER EIGHT

WHAT have I got myself into? Saunders wondered that, not for the first time, as she shifted herself to a more comfortable position in the passenger seat of the small aircraft. Not that the seat was uncomfortable, because it wasn't. It was Saunders herself who was not comfortable, and she very well knew why!

Hardly airborne, and already she was feeling the forced intimacy of being closeted in such a cramped space with Ford Landell; it was a sort of heady claustrophobia, a curious combination of apprehension and exhilaration.

Below her were the shimmering, wind-riffled waters of Bass Strait; around her, outside the safe cocoon of the little twin-engined plane, was a sky like a huge blue paddock being grazed by gigantic, fluffy white sheep. It was almost magical, a sensation from some weird fantasy.

But reality was only a glace away, where strong, lean fingers manipulated the aircraft's controls with delicate movements that were as much caress as control. Where feet shod in gleaming leather stroked the rudder controls with equal gentleness.

Behind them, the Australian mainland. Ahead, still several hours away, Tasmania and Launceston, where she was scheduled to speak this very evening. In her lap were her notes, allegedly undergoing a review but actually being ignored as she watched Ford Landell out of the corners of her eyes.

He seemed just to lounge in the pilot's seat, only his eyes moving as they scanned the waves, the sky, the horizon. He might, she thought, have been sitting in an easy chair watching television for all the tension he revealed; it was as if flying the plane was effortless, unthinking, and yet she knew it could not be so.

She fidgeted some more, then stopped as she felt his eyes on her, turned her head to be sure.

'Relax, Saunders. I'm not about to try and ravish you and fly this plane at the same time. And we're a bit short of parking spots, in case you haven't noticed.'

His smile was anything but reassuring; Saunders felt a dingo would smile like that at a rabbit held in a trap. She'd have been easier in her mind if she'd known he was only teasing, but with this man she was somehow never sure.

Three weeks since she'd last seen him, the night of Simon's speech and that amazing get-together afterwards. He had phoned her at work on the Monday, to offer this flight and advise that he'd be away a while, and again last night to confirm his return, but she hadn't actually *seen* him between Simon's visit and this morning.

Except, of course, in her mind, where he seemed to have achieved permanent resident status—against her will and very much against her better judgement. Simon's comments on the situation had helped not a bit.

'You've got a rocky road ahead with that one, my girl,' he'd said on the ride home that night. 'A very, very impressive man, which, of course, I don't need to tell you. I'm quite disenchanted, actually; all my acting skills tonight were a complete waste of time, because I'd bet anything he wasn't fooled for a minute.

'Oh, he was suitably jealous, all right, but only because he couldn't help it. It was a gut reaction, not an intellectual one. He knew exactly what sort of game I was playing.'

'So did I, and I wasn't all that impressed, Simon,' Saunders had replied. 'It was so over the top it was almost laughable; he couldn't have been deceived for a moment, surely?'

'He could have, and should have. Ninety-nine per cent of men I know would have been,' had been the surprising reply. 'That Fitzmaurice child was certainly taken in, although that, frankly, does *not* surprise me a bit.'

'Child? Simon, she's nearly my age, for goodness' sake.'

'Only on the outside, and a very pleasing outside it is, too. But there's hardly any real *adult* person there, Saunders. That one is so wrapped up in herself that the rest of the world hardly exists for her. And your boy knows it. His reaction to her is almost that of a protective, duty-bound big brother, although I wouldn't expect *you* to see that.'

Certainly not! Even the thought had been sufficient to keep her lost in silence for the remainder of their journey home, although it had also been enough to keep her awake long into what remained of the night. What she had seen of the relationship between Nadine and Ford Landell was nothing like Simon's view.

'If that woman's attitude is anything even *like* sisterly, she's incestuously inclined,' she had said over breakfast, picking up the conversation with every expectation that Simon would know what she was about. Which of course he had.

'I wasn't talking about *her* attitude, and well you

know it,' he had replied calmly, mumbling the words around a mouthful of toast. Then, more clearly, 'You'll probably never know, which is as it should be, but I'd be prepared to bet good money that the only actual sex between those two had been in her mind—and yours.'

At which Saunders had nearly choked on her own toast. Simon was known for his subtlety, but could exhibit brutal candour when it suited him.

'Don't let your emotions completely cloud your judgement, my dear,' he had said then. 'Your boy Ford Landell is a man who's hardly ever been a child, and she has never been anything else. I don't know how he got lumbered with her, but I suggest to you that she is more of an albatross round his neck than a trophy on his bedroom mantelpiece. Besides, Landell isn't the type to hunt trophies like that.'

Now, meeting those black eyes as they glinted with humour, she desperately wished for Simon's insight.

'I'm quite relaxed,' she finally replied. 'Just a bit excited is all; I've never flown in such a small plane, much less on a trip like this. And of course I've never been to Tasmania before, either. I understand it's quite beautiful, quite unique.' She was waffling, desperate to stave off the strange intimacy created in the cabin surrounding them.

'Indeed,' he replied, but it was neither acceptance nor rejection of what she'd said, merely a space in the conversation. 'If I'd known you'd never been to Tassie, I'd have tried to arrange things differently. We could have planned to spend the whole weekend, or something.'

'I'd only arranged for the one night's billeting,' Saunders replied, not meeting his eyes now, knowing that he already knew what she had arranged, knowing that what he had in mind was quite, quite different.

'Plenty of ways around that,' he said, and didn't bother to hide the mischievous gleam in his eyes. 'A whole heap of alternatives, as a matter of fact. Anything from quite posh hotels to cosy, intimate little bed and breakfast places tucked away in some astonishingly remote locations.'

'And no prizes for guessing which *you'd* choose,' Saunders replied tartly. 'Honestly, Ford, don't you ever give up?'

'Give up?' I've hardly even begun,' he replied, then turned his attention to his flying, abandoning the campaign as readily as he'd begun it. Saunders was left to pick up the conversational gauntlet herself or turn her attentions to the speech lying patiently on her lap.

'If this plane had pontoons, we could even have packed a little tent and some tucker and *really* gone bush,' he said after a few moments' silence, continuing the discussion as if the pause hadn't existed. 'Somewhere really remote, where we could——'

'Oh, stop it! We're going to Launceston so I can give my speech tonight, if you'll just let me concentrate on it. And tomorrow we're flying back; that's what you said.'

Which it had been. 'I know your mob is always a bit strapped for cash,' he'd said on the telephone when making the unexpected offer of a lift to Launceston, and in the process totally ignoring the dark cloud under which they'd parted after drinks with Simon. 'I have to fly down on business anyway, so if it helps you're more than welcome to come down with me on the Friday—we'll be there in heaps of time for you to organise your speech and all—and then we could come back some time Saturday, or whatever.'

Thinking back, Saunders realised she had paid little attention to that word 'whatever', which hadn't seemed important at the time, but now. . .

Her outburst seemed to have taken Ford by surprise, despite the fact he'd quite deliberately engineered it.

'Is it the speech that's got you all spooked?' he asked with apparent innocence. And, without waiting for a reply, 'I wouldn't have thought such a thing would bother you; you should have it down to a fine science by now, considering the way you operate in the office.'

'The office is one thing; this is quite different—for me, anyway.'

'You should have picked up a few pointers from your little mate Simon Connelly,' was the surprising rejoinder. 'Now, there's a man who knows about speechmaking. He's got it down to more than a fine science, more like an art-form.'

The remark caused Saunders to glance up with surprise. Was he being serious in complimenting Simon, or having a shot at him? Or at her? Nothing in Ford's demeanour suggested one thing or the other; he was just lolling in his seat, flying with casual skill, his attention apparently more on what he was doing than what he was saying.

Saunders studied his profile for a moment, wishing it didn't have such intense attraction for her, then chose to return to her reading, without paddling the discussion into dangerous waters.

You think I'm having a go at you, Ford thought, carefully keeping his eyes averted, focusing his attention outside the intimate confines of the aircraft cabin.

Fair enough, I suppose. But I'm not. Not really. That Connelly bloke is one of the good ones, the genuine people. A good man, and obviously a friend of long standing—a valuable and valued friend.

He smiled to himself, careful to keep the smile inside, hidden.

Which didn't stop me being jealous as hell, at first. The man is frighteningly observant, too. He twigged right off about how I feel about you, dear Saunders, although whether he told you straight or not, I don't know. But he knew. . .

The hell of it was, Ford thought, that he had instinctively *liked* Simon Connelly, even at that first encounter, when his instinctive jealousy had had his insides twisted and his black eyes positively green with the jealousy.

I'm still jealous, but only because you're so close, only because he knows you and I'm still trying to figure you out. With not the greatest of success, either. You're a complicated woman, Saunders. Like a great ball of yarn that's all full of different pieces, with ends hanging out everywhere. I keep feeling that if I could just grab the right one. . . But which one?

He risked a glance at her, head down as she studied the speech on her knee. Smiled again to himself at the masses of never-quite-tidy hair that only half concealed the long, slender neck. At first glance it was nondescript, could even have been called mousy, but within the rowdy curls were highlights of varied, more vivid colours, colours he wanted to touch, to feel against his lips.

His eyes followed the long, slender fingers as they flexed round her pen, moved along the line of her jeans-clad leg. A woman who could wear anything and look good in it, but thin, he thought, too thin. Still, she probably achieved her rigid diabetes control without medication partly through being so slim. Ford thought of his own reaction at being told he'd been slightly overweight all of his adult life, and had to stifle a chuckle at his self-righteous indignation. He weighed slightly less now, and felt the better for it too, although he'd never admit it to Saunders, or even her dietitian.

He looked at Saunders again, then abruptly shifted his attention to flying when she seemed about to catch him observing her. There was plenty of time for that, he thought, before this trip was over.

Saunders, under the guise of reworking her speech for the evening, was free to wonder yet again about the erratic, tumultuous relationship which was evolving between them.

Not for the first time, she wished she had somehow met Landell outside her professional situation. It seemed to her a quite unnecessary distraction and one which had somehow coloured their entire relationship thus far.

And it shouldn't, she thought.

To Saunders, her diabetes, while certainly serious enough, was something she seldom consciously thought of or worried about. It existed, it could be managed quite easily and, with a pragmatism granted by her profession and her particular temperament, that had always been sufficient. Until Ford Landell had leapt into the equation, with his philosophical questions and his ability to turn her inside-out with a single touch.

Now she found that the very existence of the medical condition they shared was simply too often a distraction; it crept into the relationship at unpredictable times and circumstances. Like when Ford had rung to ask if she wanted to fly to Tasmania. . .or after, rather. She had accepted willingly, perhaps too willingly, she now thought. But afterwards she had found it impossible to keep from wondering. There was no reason for him not to be flying, provided he had his condition under proper control and recognised the very tiny risks that might be involved. But did he? Certainly she couldn't ask, but the question niggled.

As did the questions he'd brought up at that first professional consultation, about how relevant heredity might be in his future relationships. At the time she had thought them so premature as to be hardly relevant, but they had hovered in the back of her mind ever since. And, worse, they had insisted that she view them from her own perspective as well. Before meeting Ford she had seldom so much as considered having children, except in sort of vague generalities. Now she found herself occasionally giving the issue serious thought, and she was concerned at her reactions.

Pregnancy, she knew, always had an element of risk. Diabetes marginally increased the risk factor, but not by any startling degree. The real risk, she thought, was in how prospective parents viewed the problem, or created the problem, in how they viewed the overall situation.

Ford Landell wanted children. He hadn't come right out and said so, but it was implicit in his attitudes, complicated somewhat by his own orphaned start in life, and now even more so by his having developed diabetes. Was the fact that she, too, had the condition merely a complication? Or something for which 'merely' wasn't an adequate description?

The whole situation ran round and round through her mind like a devilish mouse in a treadmill cage. All exercise and no solution whatsoever, she thought. Because no solution was possible.

If nothing else, it had given her the topic for her speech tonight. She'd selected the theme and done most of the work before Ford's offer of a lift, had had grave second thoughts when she realised he might be among her audience, but found herself with neither the time to change topics or—being totally honest— the desire. Once into the subject, she had found it a classic, an issue raised by every client she'd dealt with.

And now here I am, she thought, soaring across Bass Strait in a flying tin can, with the man who's responsible for the best speech I've ever prepared— and I can't even talk to him about it!

It was a moment later when she suddenly realised she would have to fly *back* with him too, and that if he attended her speech, she might have no choice but to talk about it.

'Damn,' she said, and didn't realise she had spoken aloud until she heard Ford reply.

'If it's causing you that much worry,' he said, without looking directly at her, 'why don't you try it out on me first?'

'Try out what?' she replied, momentarily confused because she had been thinking about what to say to him *after* the speech, not the speech itself.

'Your speech, of course. Or isn't that what you were cursing? If it was my flying abilities, for example, maybe you'd best wait until after we get there; I don't take criticism very well.'

'Even if it's constructive?' Saunders asked, leaping at this tiny chance to change the subject.

'Especially if it's constructive! Constructive criticism is usually just another word for free advice, and you can take it from me that advice is usually worth just about as much as it costs.'

'So, if I was to try out my speech on you, whatever advice you'd give me wouldn't be worth anything? Or haven't you established the price yet?'

'It wouldn't be worth a brass razoo. If I were to give you any—either free advice or constructive criticism, that is—which I wouldn't even presume to do.' His voice was soft, almost gentle, and he wasn't looking at her when he spoke, but kept his attention on the job of flying the aircraft. 'Really, Saunders. How could I offer you advice or criticism on something you know ten times more about than I do?'

'Well, then, where's the logic of me trying out the speech on you?' she demanded. 'You're not making much sense, if you don't mind me saying so.'

'All the sense in the world. You haven't, I'd bet, tried out your speech on an audience of any kind. Which means even *you* can only guess at how it will sound, how it will flow, which words might be worth changing to improve the cadence, which elements might be swapped round to make it hang together better. You've only done it in your head, and that, dear Saunders, isn't the same thing at all.'

All of which was true, and she knew it. Because she had been there before and been caught; usually she tried out her infrequent speeches on some innocent staff member, not for the acceptance that automatically followed, but because it gave her the chance for self-criticism. What Ford was suggesting was exactly that, except. . .

'But if I went all through the speech now, you

wouldn't be able to come and listen to me do it properly,' she protested. 'Assuming, of course, that you were planning to come along tonight. . .'

'I wouldn't miss it for the world,' he replied with a slow grin. 'Unless, of course, you'd rather I didn't come?'

'I. . . Well. . . It's up to you, of course,' Saunders replied, not really sure how to continue. 'But I can't imagine you wanting to hear the entire speech twice.'

Strong fingers reached across the tiny cockpit to touch her forearm. The gesture was meant to be soothing, reassuring, she thought, but in actuality it only stirred her more, as did the words that followed.

'If it's as good a speech as I would expect from you, twice won't hurt a bit,' he said. 'And if I get bored, I can always just sit and look at you, can't I?'

Caught by the teasing expression in his voice, Saunders looked over to catch him looking at her *now*, his entire attention focused, it seemed, on exploring her face, her hair, her shoulders, her breasts, her entire body, with eyes that smouldered with ill-repressed laughter.

Saunders could not laugh in reply; there was nothing funny about the way her body reacted to Ford's visual caresses. His touch had sent goosebumps spiralling from wrist to shoulder; she couldn't help the compulsive shudder that followed, wanted to flinch away from that touch. . .or into it. Indeed, she must have flinched, because the papers on her lap slid off, to flutter down and land in a muddle around her feet.

'Now see what you've made me do,' she muttered, leaning forward in a vain attempt to capture the papers, then to pick them up. Only to rear upright again as his fingers lifted to touch the back of her neck,

pushing aside the wild mane of hair and sliding along
her skin like a whispered kiss.

Saunders' hand dipped forward, her neck twisting as
she writhed beneath that sensual, almost unbearable
caress. She felt rather than heard the low moan of
pleasure that crept up into her throat, felt also the
searing flutter of excitement that flowed from her nape
to the very centre of her being, where everything was
turning to a whirlpool of sensation.

It was as if she were paralysed, unable to straighten
against the light, magic touch of his fingers on her
neck. She felt herself leaning forward, submissively,
her elbows on her knees and her head bowed to allow
his fingers all the freedom they wished.

His voice whispered, but she heard only a soothing,
wind-blown sound; no words seemed involved. His
hand moved so that his fingers touched behind her
ears, gripping lightly but firmly as the fingertips mas-
saged there. Then the massage moved lower, flexing
along the length of her neck, easing the tensions she
hadn't even known existed. She felt the magic as he
manipulated along her shoulders, first the one and
then the other, his fingers strong and yet ever so
gentle, ever so magical in their touch.

Saunders remained still, eyes shut, floating magically within the touch of Ford's massage, even as the
two of them and their aircraft floated magically above
the frothy waters of Bass Strait. It was as if she were
hypnotised; everything around her disappeared—the
sound of the aircraft was muted, there was no sensation of movement, or. . .anything. Just the magic of
the fingers stroking, caressing, manipulating her neck.
It was as if her bones had turned to water; she had
difficulty even maintaining her balance.

Then his hand moved lower, his strong fingers stroking a tune down the nubbins of her spine, a tune in which each note seemed to thrust down into the depths of her, touching nerves she hadn't even known existed. She sighed, heard herself moan again in the pleasure of it, knew she was beyond all control now, didn't care.

'Saunders.'

He said her name, his voice far away, barely audible, but speaking in a tone she had never before heard from him, a tone filled with wanting, needing, a tone as soft as his caresses.

'Saunders.'

Harsher now. And the caresses of his fingers had halted too. When he spoke her name a third time, she straightened up, tried to respond.

'Saunders? Are you all right?'

All right? She would never again be all right, she thought, but nodded agreement with a neck that seemed to have no muscles in it.

'I'm fine, really.'

'I thought for a moment you'd dropped off,' he said, and it was too soon for her to even to try to meet his eyes. Saunders kept her head down, her eyes averted.

'I must have been a bit more tense that I would have thought,' she finally managed to say. Then wondered why, because even the words didn't make much sense.

'I don't think "tense" is exactly the word,' Ford said, and reached over to place his fingers beneath her chin, lifting her head and forcing her to look at him.

Those eyes! Like deep black pools of iridescent ink, they were. And they spoke to her just as his fingers had, telling her that he knew what she'd been feeling, knew how she had reacted to his touch, to his caresses. He knew!

'Saunders, I. . .' He paused, then, holding back for some reason. But now Saunders knew—was *certain*— he was about to say what she so desperately needed to hear. He was about to put into the words the emotions and feelings he had been displaying through his caresses.

But the moment was lost; his dark eyes left hers, shifted past her, to where a faint, greeny-grey smudge of colour was peering through between riffled sea and cotton-wool cloud-banks.

'Flinders Island,' he said. 'Not that long now, and you'll be back on firm ground.'

To which Saunders could easily have replied, I've just come to earth with an almighty thump already, and yet I'm still up here in the air. But she didn't. Instead, she swallowed her disappointment and pretended enthusiasm as Ford swung the plane in a sweeping pass over Flinders Island and the rest of the Furneaux Group, then headed south-west on a long curve to Launceston, and the airport south of the city.

Forgotten, apparently, was his suggestion that she try her speech out on him. More important to Saunders, he also seemed to have forgotten whatever he'd been about to say as they had come into sight of land. Instead, he now turned into a sort of tour-guide, relating the various landmarks and scenic attractions as they appeared.

Saunders listened, observed, but only with half a mind. She had shifted into a mental wasteland, not quite in the present but not quite anywhere else either. It seemed her brain was stalled, numbed by the sensations of her emotions—emotions that Ford

Landell had somehow taken to the brink and then abandoned there.

He spoke intermittently into the radio, circled the airport at Western Junction, just south of Launceston, eventually landed and drew the aircraft up to a private hangar. Saunders disembarked, took the various baggage he handed out to her, waited patiently and almost unthinkingly while he went to telephone for a taxi. When it arrived, they got in and drove into the city's southern suburbs, eventually halting before a suburban house on a suburban street that could have been almost anywhere.

Ford had the cabbie wait, and Saunders sat patiently, calmly, watching as he opened the garage and clambered up into a decrepit, dilapidated old Land Rover, apparently with the intention of getting it started.

'I was afraid of that,' he said on his return a moment later. 'It's been a while since I was here, and the old girl'll need a bit of work before she comes good. I'm going to send you on with the cab, Saunders, because you have more important things to do while I play motor mechanic. I'll catch up at tonight's meeting—promise!'

He hefted out his own luggage from the boot, gave the cabbie directions to the local diabetes centre, then leaned in through the passenger window to kiss Saunders lightly, casually, and quite unexpectedly, on the lips.

'Gee, you're beautiful,' he said. 'You'll knock 'em dead tonight, no matter what you say.'

And before she could reply, while her lips still held the imprint of his kiss and her mind was trying to interpret his last remarks, he waved the taxi away.

She was still pondering whether those remarks had been compliments, insults, or something far, far more important than either, when the taxi arrived at its destination and she had to focus her mind on the task ahead of her instead of the baffling, intriguing, infuriating man she had just left behind.

In the flurry of meeting her compatriots, her billeting hosts for the night and the various other folk involved with the meeting, she managed quite nicely, she thought, to push Ford firmly to the back of her mind and keep him there. Until she found herself at the podium, facing a crowd ten times larger than any she had ever before addressed, and immediately found him sitting in the front row, listening intently, encouraging her with his eyes, his bearing, his very presence, as she launched into a speech that might have been written with only Ford Landell and herself in mind.

Ford was the anchor for her speech. No other face in the large audience held form for her; no one else even really existed. She spoke exclusively to him, aiming each word, each inflexion, all the passion of her genuine beliefs—all at him! He became a sort of conduit, conveying her words, her attitudes, to the crowd around him. It was, she knew, when it was finally over, the finest such speech she would ever give, had ever given. Because of him.

CHAPTER NINE

'I HAD nothing to do with it!'

'Oh, but you did. I didn't have a chance to tell you last night, and I. . .I meant to,' Saunders replied. 'You have no idea how much difference it made, having somebody I *knew* there in the front, somebody I could focus on.'

'And I suppose it never occurred to you that I was only sitting in the front row so I could look up your skirt?'

Ford's comment was so matter-of-fact, his tone so quietly conversational, that Saunders didn't, for a moment, realise exactly what he'd said. And, when she did twig, she looked over to see him sitting with a perfectly straight face and his eyes never leaving the road ahead.

This, she decided, was yet another side to Ford Landell that she hadn't realised existed. They had been arguing gently ever since setting out at dawn on the sightseeing venture he'd promised her before they flew back to the mainland.

There had been no time for any personal talk after her speech; Ford had politely hovered until he'd had the opportunity to offer quick congratulations, meet her hostess and arrange to pick Saunders up in the morning, then had pleaded work in progress and disappeared. This morning he'd been rather more effusive in his congratulations, but had refused to accept any personal credit whatsoever.

And now this. . .

All right, thought Saunders. If you want to play games, we'll play games.

'You enjoyed the view, though? Good legs, you thought?'

Now it was his turn to pause before cautiously replying.

'That's a strange question.'

'Not really,' she said. 'I just wondered if you would have preferred oak, or maybe pine. That's all.'

'On you? I rather doubt it, Saunders.'

'On the podium I was standing *behind* the entire time,' she said then, suddenly a bit unsure who had been leading whom down which garden path.

'I did think the ankles were just a bit thick.' He turned to flash his most dazzling smile across the dingy interior of the Land Rover, forcing Saunders to laugh and admit defeat.

'But seriously,' he said after a moment, his eyes back on the highway as he steered through the Breadalbane roundabout and headed south, 'I really would like us to spend this day just being *people*. No nurse-patient relationship, no blood sugar levels, no glucometers, no diabetes principles, no speeches. . . Just two people playing tourist. What do you reckon?'

Saunders looked across at him, but he kept his face impassive, his eyes firmly on the highway ahead. But there was, she could see, evidence of tension in the taut tendons of his muscular neck, in the grip of those strong, tanned hands on the steering-wheel.

'Agreed,' she said after long consideration, then reached out to take the hand he offered her. A brief shake, an equally brief flash of firm white teeth, then she was left to wonder if all 'tourists' drove through the Tasmanian countryside in such a strained, disquieting silence.

The silence lasted down through Campbelltown, where they turned left on to a narrow stretch of bitumen called the Lake Leake Road, but gradually the feeling of strain disappeared. Ford's silence was merely vocal; he smilingly pointed out newborn lambs, a soaring hawk, a higher-soaring eagle, a flock of white cockatoos floating down into a paddock like so much popcorn into a great green bowl.

It became a companionable silence, a comfortable silence, in which Saunders found herself relaxing, enjoying the relative quiet of the journey, the lack of traffic, the unhurried pace at which they travelled.

The road they travelled was meandering eastward now, and gradually climbing from the rolling midlands into the higher timbered country that—according to the map he had passed over to her—eventually fell away to the island's east coast.

'We'll go waterfalling first, and then if there's time we can do a bit of fossicking; I know a good place for it.'

The remark came from nowhere, surprised Saunders so much that she flinched in her seat, then realised she had been almost asleep. Ford had slowed down, was turning into an information bay that, upon inspection, listed several waterfalls in the vicinity.

Ten minutes later they were at Lost Falls. 'Which I reckon were hardly worth finding,' said Ford after a short walk to where they could look a long way down at a relatively insignificant cascade of water in a small creek. 'Still, it's here, and who knows when, if ever, we might come this way again?'

The futuristic sentiments in that comment touched

some spark in Saunders, as had the touch of Ford's
hand as he'd guided her out of the Land Rover and
had continued to hold her hand until the narrow trail
to the look-out made such action difficult.

Meetus Falls, on the Cygnet Rivulet headwaters of
the Swan River, about fifteen kilometres to the north,
was much more spectacular—well worth the twenty-
minute round-trip hike to the look-out platform. Here,
the insignificant stream they had crossed on the gravel
road *en route* was transformed into a wind-whipped,
shimmering curtain as it tumbled over the escarpment
into a pool of mist far below them.

But for Saunders, that day and forever, it was
Hardings Falls on the upper Swan River, the third
place they visited, which had the greatest impact.

It was nearly eleven by the time they got to the tiny
parking area on a scrubby ridge of the coastal escarpment, and it was getting exceptionally warm.

'Just as well; I'm not sure I'd want to be driving this
road in the wet,' Ford had muttered as the old Land
Rover shuddered and shook along the rutted, red dirt
track which allegedly continued on to join the coastal
highway far below and to the east.

He descended from the vehicle, stretched mightily
and, after opening the rear doors, began to assemble a
day-pack.

'We'll have lunch by the water, and maybe a swim if
the river isn't insanely cold,' he said. 'I'm going to
change before we go, too. It's a fair old hike to the
bottom, here, and not much of a track either. It'll be
damned hot walking, I expect. Especially coming
back.'

Saunders was left to watch—or not—as he sat on
the bumper bar, peeled off his hiking-boots, then

matter-of-factly stripped off jumper and jeans. The tanned, muscular body thus revealed was, she decided, definitely worth a look, although she also made a mental note to have her dietitian's eyesight checked. How Diane could have considered this man overweight was beyond her comprehension.

Ford pulled on a pair of well-worn football shorts, tugged a T-shirt over his tousled hair, then knelt to replace the hiking-boots, peering upward at Saunders as he did so.

'You going like that?' he asked, then pointed to the day-pack. 'We'll be stopping for lunch at the bottom, assuming we get there without breaking a leg. You'll be far too hot, I warn you.'

There was a curious expression in his eyes, she imagined. Something approaching a dare, or, at the very least, a private, secret laughter. She refused to let herself be drawn to comment, merely turned to throw open her flight-bag and search inside for lighter clothing for herself.

But, having searched out her own light tank-top and shorts, a second glance at Ford—so clearly in expectation of being an audience to her changing—gave her second thoughts. Ignoring his cheeky grin, she stepped to the opposite side of the vehicle to give herself some privacy, only to find that she might escape his eyes, but not his voice.

'Shy, Miss White? I really wouldn't have expected it.' And his voice was teasing, bantering. It wasn't possible to decide if he was just having a chuckle at her or making a more serious point.

Whichever, Saunders determined to try and make light of the situation, otherwise it was poised to get far too serious, more so, in her opinion, than it deserved, and far more than she wanted.

'It isn't that I'm shy,' she managed to reply. 'It's that you, sir, are a dirty old man and quite probably a pervert, and I daren't encourage you.'

Which was a silly thing to say, and she realised it when she returned around the vehicle and had to endure the deliberate, provocative challenge in those black, black eyes as he ran them over her from top to bottom and back again.

By comparison with his own out-of-doors tan, she expected she must look pale and anaemic, Saunders thought, suddenly distinctly shy as Ford's eyes revealed his appreciation.

Especially when he nodded and said, 'I take it all back; you're not a bit too skinny—not one bit.' Which was only a tiny, tiny bit of what those dark eyes said as they skimmed her bare white skin like butterfly wings.

'I wonder. . .' he said then, and immediately turned to start rummaging through the interior of the vehicle. When he emerged with a satisfied grunt and locked up the vehicle, he held in his hands a crumpled towelling cap and a small tube of some ointment.

'Come here,' he said with a curious little grin, and waved imperiously when Saunders didn't immediately obey. And when she did eventually go to him, he thrust the towelling cap atop her unruly curls and stepped back to survey the result.

'Definitely you, Miss White,' he chuckled. 'Now, just one more small detail and we can set off on this wondrous journey.'

And before she could even think to resist, he was

once again close in front of her, reaching out to lift her sunglasses away and put them into her protesting hand.

'Skin as fair as yours should never be risked,' he said in a strangely soft voice, his eyes only inches away from her own as he squeezed a bit of the ointment on to his fingers and began to smooth it gently over her face.

Saunders couldn't have objected had she wanted to; he held her captive with his eyes, with the oily touch of his fingers as he stroked at her forehead, her cheekbones, the bridge of her nose, her chin, and finally along the slope of her neck, to spread the sunblock cream on to her shoulders and upper arms.

His touch there was no longer soft; he rubbed in the cream energetically, only letting his fingers linger when they crossed the points of her collarbones. When he nodded for her to turn, she did so, and again he eschewed tenderness in favour of being thorough, as he plastered the stuff on the exposed portions of her shoulders and back.

'Right. Let's get going,' he said then, abandoning her to thrust the sunscreen into the day-pack, which he hoisted to one shoulder, then he waved the other hand magnanimously in the direction of the signposted track to the falls.

Saunders preceded him, both amused and angry with herself for the strange feelings of shyness that Ford seemed so adept at creating. I'm like a sixteen-year-old on her first date, she thought, absolutely certain that her reaction was totally obvious to the man walking along behind her. In her self-consciousness, she stumbled occasionally over nothing on the well-defined trail that crossed half a dozen tiny bridges of treated pine as it wound beneath large, spreading casuarines and towering gum trees.

The scrub got thicker as they neared the edge of the escarpment and Saunders could hear, increasing in volume, the sound of flowing water off to her right and ahead. A bit further and they suddenly moved out on to a rough point of rocks, scattered with seeming haphazard manner, and a few cautious steps more brought her to a ragged, stumbling halt. Below and to her left she could see the stream moving into a large, obviously deep bowl, while a continuation of the rocks ahead camouflaged the water's exit to continue downward. . .and downward. . .and downward.

She couldn't see anything of a waterfall proper, but to her right—and far lower down than the pool—there were enormous rock-slabs, and the occasional glint of flowing water between, then a rush of white-water and another gigantic pool far down the cliff.

'I'd best go ahead now. The track doesn't look any better than the last time I was here, and it can be a trifle threatening,' said Ford, who had stepped up beside her. He turned away to his right and began cautiously picking his way down what Saunders could only just perceive as some sort of winding, switchback trail down the scree slope.

The trail turned out, thankfully, to look much more difficult than it actually was. But it none the less took them a fair time, Saunders thought, carefully to negotiate their path over the treacherous rubble, winding back and forth with never a proper view of the waterfall itself until they finally reached the bottom.

But then it was all worth it, ten times over, she thought. Moving on to the water-worn bottom of the gorge itself, forced to hop over great crevasses and around what appeared to be rainwater pools, they rounded the corner to find themselves faced with a vast panorama of falling waters.

The ridge where they had started off spread right across the valley, and water poured down in a multitude of different places. Some came down in distinct, spray-misted falls, more seemed to spring from the rock itself in tiny trickles, delicate tracings and rippling cascades.

'There's been a good deal more rain up-country somewhere than I would have thought from looking at the road,' Ford commented, leading the way to where a deep, dark pool snuggled beneath clouds of mist and spray before opening out into a white-water run through various smaller pools and eventually to a series of larger ones further below them again.

Ford dropped the pack in a safe place where the base rock had split into a natural table and seats, then wandered along the edge of the frothing currents, apparently lost in contemplation, observing the water, the rock formations, occasionally glancing upward at the surrounding canyon.

Saunders did her own bit of wandering, carefully clambering along until she was as close beneath the main waterfall as she could get, looking upward to where the high sun was making a myriad rainbows through the spray. It was, she found, amazingly invigorating—unexpectedly, splendidly so.

She was standing, staring down into the main pool at the huge boulders strewn across the bottom, when she sensed Ford's approach, even before he stopped behind her and placed his hands gently at her waist.

'Lunch first, or swim first?' he asked.

'Lunch, definitely,' she replied, not bothering to

explain that this swimming fantasy of his could be no more than that. She hadn't brought swimming gear, was reasonably sure he hadn't either, and had no intention whatsoever of going skinny-dipping, even in such a delightful setting.

But when Ford began to disperse the contents of his day-pack, she honestly wondered if he mightn't have swimming costumes in there for both of them—he seemed to have just about everything else!

Crusty wholemeal rolls, crackers and dips, half a dozen varieties of exotic cheese, pickles, olives, even a thermos of steaming coffee, were produced with a magician's *élan*, along with napkins, a selection of cutlery, a corkscrew and a bottle of vintage Piper's Brook wine.

'I am suitably impressed,' Saunders said, and meant it.

'So you should be,' was the smiling reply. 'Especially by the Piper's Brook—it's so in demand for export you can hardly ever seem to get it locally.'

They ate most of their meal in silence, seemingly both content just to absorb the quiet serenity of their situation. Saunders, who would have sworn at the outset that she was only a touch peckish, not really hungry at all, did full justice to her share of the repast; it was no surprise to see Ford getting through his.

It was sheer bliss but, like the meal, it had to end, and it did, for Saunders, when Ford finished clearing up the remains and rose to this feet with a suddenly ominous litheness.

'Now, madam—swim?' he asked. And she knew it was more than the sun's rays putting that dangerous little gleam in his eyes.

'I. . . We. . . Not so soon after eating, surely?' she

stammered, speaking the first halfway legitimate objection that came to mind, knowing—and knowing that *he* knew—exactly what she was doing, what she was thinking.

'That business of not exercising too soon after eating is nothing but an old wives' tail, and well you know it. I think you're just fishing for excuses. Like the fact you don't happen to have a swimsuit either,' Ford replied with a wry grin, staring down at her from what now seemed an enormous height. Laughing at her, scoffing at her, she thought.

'Well, do *you*?' she retorted, only to realise what a terribly silly question that was, given the circumstances. All *he* really needed to do was shed his T-shirt and boots, if it came to that; for her actually to swim was just slightly more complicated.

She looked up, met his eyes, and could have killed him for the way he laughed down at her, for the way he raised one dark eyebrow as he shook his head. And then, unreasoningly, she reached up to grasp the hand he extended and allowed herself to be lifted to her feet, felt his free hand coil around her waist.

'You're a funny girl, Saunders,' he said, bending to whisper the words into her ear, turning her against him, holding her far too close.

And, before she could even think, he calmly tipped them both into the icy waters of the pool, laughing wildly as they landed with a mighty splash.

The suddenness and the chill took Saunders' breath away. She was thoroughly submerged for only a second or two, but was gasping when she surfaced, still locked in Ford's embrace, and still gasping when he gripped her waist and hoisted her up to sit on the rock edging the pool, with her hair plastered down over her eyes and water streaming everywhere.

As she struggled to drag the hair back from her eyes, with fingers numb from surprise more than the cold water, Ford slid out of the water like an otter, and was sitting there with the most amazing grin on his face when she finally managed to see.

'Are you right out of your mind?' she cried, damp hair in one hand and her sunglasses, having miraculously survived the ordeal, waving in the other. 'Oh. . . Ford—the hat!'

Even as she spoke, the towelling cap was swirling in a small side-eddy, clearly *en route* in a continued journey down the stream as it revolved towards where the foot of the pool narrowed to dive over a narrow outcropping of rock.

Saunders could feel the goosebumps rising like hives all over her, but the chill didn't seem to bother her companion, who laughed as he slid back into the water and smoothly stroked his way over to retrieve the cap at the last possible instant.

He returned to float beside Saunders' feet, tossing the cap on to the rock shelf beside her, and then adroitly slipped off his boots and tossed them, too, up on to dry rock.

'It's not as cold as it seems at first,' he said with a deceptive grin, reaching up as if to drag her back into the icy water with him.

Saunders squealed and tried to twist herself completely on to the rock shelf, but she was too late. Ford had one hand round her ankle and seemed set for a tug of war she could only lose. When she kicked out with her free leg, he reached up to grab that one too, and laughed at her frantic attempts to free herself.

'Don't be such a sissy,' he said, reaching to remove her sodden shoes and toss them up beside his own. And then he somehow managed to manoeuvre himself so that he was resting with his arms across her thighs, his head tipped back so that he could laugh up into her eyes. It was a strangely intimate position, made more so when he casually turned to lay his lips against her tummy where the saturated tank-top had ridden up.

After the icy immersion his lips had an unusual warmth, as did the arms that now encircled her hips and the chest that burned like fire against her upper thighs.

'Stop that.' But she didn't really mean it; even as she spoke her fingers were entwining themselves in his damp, rumpled hair, touching—at first tentatively, and then with growing urgency—at where the sun was already drying his muscular neck and shoulders.

'Stop,' she said again. But now his lips were moving along her tummy, trailing sensation in their wake. And his fingers were now beneath the tank-top, stroking her bare back just where the base of her spine was lost in the swelling of her hips. Those fingers moved in a gentle, rhythmic, circular motion, tantalising, mesmerising.

Stop. . .oh. . .stop. But only her mind cried out now. Ford had shifted his position, so that now his lips could reach the soft portions of her upper thighs, plundering, looting, destroying whatever good intentions still existed. Not many.

Ford's strong hands manipulated Saunders as if she were a puppet, a doll. If he had wished to pull her into the water, to make love to her *under* the water, he would have faced no real resistance. Nor did he when he slid away, just far enough to tip her on her side, so that she lay on the waterside rock, her mouth captured by his own as her head was cradled in his left arm and his other hand was free to explore her body as a guide for his lips in future.

And the future was now! His fingers trailed across her throat, down through the soft hollows below her collarbones, across the still wet tank-top and the bra that her body now wished she hadn't worn. His lips followed, guided as much by the writhings of her own body as by his fingers. The wet clothing was little hindrance to her erect, turgid nipples, even less to the sensitivity of her breasts.

His moth-wing touch was all-encompassing; his kisses and his fingers flowed like soothing water over her calves, her knees, in delicious currents along the softness of her inner thighs. She writhed to ease the task of fingers that unclipped her bra, that lifted the tank-top to release her swollen breasts to his lips.

There was a momentary hesitation as he slid from the water in a single, fluid action, only to lie beside her, the entire damp length of him cool and then hot against her body as their limbs entwined.

Somehow, then, their lovemaking took on a time-less quality, as if they were drugged by the sun's heat, the stronger heat from their own enraptured bodies. Saunders' hands roamed of their own volition along the muscular planes of Ford's body, slithering beneath the damp T-shirt, easing their way up his thighs, revelling in their effect on the firm evidence of his need.

But what few clothes they wore were an enhance-ment rather than a hindrance, and gradually Saunders sensed that, despite his needs, Ford was actually in some semblance of control; he was guiding her, guid-ing himself, orchestrating their desires, their reactions.

'Look at me,' he whispered, and stilled his eager, roaming hands from their journey along her ribcage until she had to open her eyes, had to meet and absorb and understand the expression in those black, black eyes only inches away from her own.

'You're beautiful. . .so beautiful,' he said, and now his voice was more than a whisper as his kiss followed the words, his tongue probing, searching with her own, as his fingers searched, as his strong masculinity searched against her groin.

'I want you. . .so much.'

What was stopping him? she wondered. Certainly not her! She was beyond stopping, beyond thinking; she could only react to his kisses, to his touch, to the way he felt beneath her fingers, against her skin.

Saunders opened her eyes again, aware of his kisses on her throat, on her breasts. Opened them to see the sky above filled with flowing, billowing white clouds, to see the plumes of spray being whipped away from the cliff where the waters plunged down. Opened them to see. . .

And then—to hear! And the sound of that whistle—no birdsong, but a distinctly, obviously *human* whistle—brought her head around to where she could see, far above, the crest of the ridge above the fall, the grey rock now capped with colourful, moving figures—*human* figures.

Ford's weight shifted above her. Had he heard it too? But his lips didn't stop their exploration, moving enticingly along her tummy, then higher. She ignored them, her eyes fixed on the ridge-top as her arms worked free, her hands moved down against the bulk of his chest. All the magic was gone now. Her entire attention was focused not on Ford, not on her reaction to his caresses, but on the embarrassment that flooded like ice over everything.

'Stop,' she said. Or tried to. She was never sure if the word had emerged audibly or not. Didn't care. Didn't care, either, that he hadn't seemed to hear her, that he hadn't also heard the whistle, could not see the waving arms as one observer pointed out to another the performance below—*their* performance.

'Stop, damn it!'

But she didn't wait, now, to see if he'd heard. She didn't know and didn't care. Her arms were in place between them, her position was right. She shoved, forcing the heels of her hands against his chest and pushing as hard as she could.

There was an instant when she heard his cry of astonishment, but it was overshadowed quickly by the roar of even greater surprise as his body struck the chilly water and submerged with a mighty splash.

Saunders was already scrambling to her feet, fingers flying to adjust her still damp clothing, when Ford's head emerged from the water. He was thrashing his way to the edge, beginning to clamber out, when the wave of cheers and clapping and the shrieks of encouragement flowed down from the heights in a humiliating tide.

Ford caught it halfway out of the water. He looked at the ridge, with its scalp-lock of spectators, looked at Saunders, who was crouched, red-faced and angry, as she fumbled for her shoes and hissed at him in the most potent curses she knew.

She had risen to her feet, was facing him with only a few feet separating them. He was looking back and forth, his dark eyes flashing from Saunders to the cheering audience on the ridge and back again, and she could see his mouth twitching, could see the devils laughing behind his eyes. She closed her eyes momentarily in disbelief as he waved, opened them again to see him execute a sweeping theatrical bow, heard the now thunderous applause.

And when he bowed for the second time she rushed at him without warning, her mind numbed with amazement at his sheer audacity.

She struck him just as he straightened up, caught him with her hands and her shoulder, overbalanced herself, felt his fingers close on her wrist, but didn't care as this time both of them plunged into the pool.

He still held her wrist when they surfaced, but released her in mute obedience to her hiss of command, and with the sinuous grace of an otter he flowed up on to the rock and stood, reaching down to help her out. And he was still laughing!

Saunders flung back her head, dipping her hair to take it away from her face. And, as she did so, the sheer absurdity of it all struck her, so that when she emerged again her own snarl had magically turned to a grin.

'If you take another bow, I shall kill you,' she growled as Ford lifted her to stand beside him on the rocks. 'I may do it anyway.'

'No, your turn, I think,' he said, ignoring the last part of her remark. 'And probably a curtsy would be more appropriate, if I may suggest it.'

Whereupon he took the fingers of one hand in his own, led her round to face the cliff-top, and waved for silence before he balanced her as she dipped in a curtsy that, she thought, was every bit as flamboyant as his bow.

And the audience loved it.

CHAPTER TEN

'IT REALLY was not all *that* funny.'

Saunders' sense of humour had evaporated somewhat during the long climb back from the gorge, and Ford's occasional chuckle as they drove was starting to get on her nerves.

Bad enough to have been sprung by that party of student rock-climbers, worse to have been forced to climb the precarious track past youthful smiles and knowing glances, however friendly, sympathetic and even envious.

Emotional reaction had begun to set in when she began the climb, walking ahead of Ford and thus the first to encounter their descending audience. Saunders had felt exposed, more vulnerable than she could ever remember, and it had only been marginally gratifying to receive the approving looks sent her by the male members of the climbing group. The girls had been a somewhat different story; almost without exception they had looked first at Ford, then shot *very* impressed, *very* approving glances at Saunders as they passed. One girl had given her a definite thumbs-up signal, and another had mouthed a discreet, 'Good one!' as she'd stepped aside to give Saunders room.

Not one of the party, she thought, would have been past nineteen, but it had been all too clear that not one had been in the slightest misled about the unusual sighting their expedition had turned up.

'OK,' said Ford, glancing across the vehicle at her

with eyes that said he lied, 'it wasn't, as such, all *that* funny. But what else could you do but laugh? It's certainly not something I'd want to cry about.'

'How about simply not becoming the centre of attention in the first place?' Saunders retorted. Then her mind went back to the night of the Mahoneys' party and she added ruefully, 'Or is that one of your chief claims to fame—public displays of lust?'

'That's a low blow, Saunders,' Ford replied. 'Is it my fault you're so completely irresistible that I can't help kissing you?'

'Well, it certainly isn't mine! You make it sound as if I go about just blatantly encouraging you,' she said, only to recoil hastily as he snapped back quickly.

'Well, you do!'

'I do no such thing.'

'Of course you do. I've already told you you're irresistible. I just can't help myself; I look at you and I want to take you in my arms and kiss you and. . .'

'And you're absolutely shameless,' she said.

Ford seemed taken aback by that remark; he drove in silence for a moment, not taking his eyes from the road ahead, but in her side vision Saunders could see his jaw muscles working, and even fancied she could hear his teeth grinding.

'I do hope,' he said finally, his voice calm but flat, 'that you aren't going to tell me you're ashamed at people seeing you being kissed. Because I'm certainly not, Saunders, and you ought to know that. There is nothing shameful about it!'

Now it was Saunders' turn to pause; the conversation had taken a turn she didn't much like. It had never been her intention to insult Ford, and now it seemed she might have.

'I wasn't suggesting you should be ashamed,' she finally said. 'And I wasn't saying that I am, either. Just that it's a bit. . .disconcerting, I guess, to have an audience every time you do it.'

His laugh was genuine, but somehow not encouraging. Nor was the way he suddenly yanked at the steering-wheel and spun the old Land Rover to a halt on the wide gravel shoulder of the road.

His left arm snaked out to surround her shoulders, drawing her in close to him. His right hand reached out to cradle her chin, forcing her to meet his eyes.

'Right!' he said. 'Now, I want you to look ahead up the road, and then look back, and then admit that there isn't a vehicle in sight and we haven't seen one— not a single one—in twenty minutes. OK?'

Saunders did as she was asked, admitting only to herself that she was far more conscious just at that moment of the texture of his cheek as her head moved past it, of the clean, strong line of his muscular neck.

'Admit it!'

'All right, I admit it,' she sighed, her lips already half prepared for his kiss, only her stubborn nature remotely opposed to it. She didn't want to look at the road in either direction; she wanted to look at his eyes, to see the wanting, the needing, the emotions she needed to see there.

'And don't kiss with your eyes open,' he said, after a lifetime in which his own eyes had played as strong a role as his lips, his delicate fingertips.

Saunders backed away fractionally, just enough to let her mouth move.

'But why not? *You* do. How else would you be able to——'

'Because it makes me think you're looking for the

audience,' he said. 'It's OK for me, because I'm only looking at you.'

'But I——'

He stopped that argument with his mouth, not a particularly difficult task. And this time Saunders kept her eyes shut.

This kiss, perhaps because of her eyes being closed, was different from the one before. Deeper, more intimate, infinitely more satisfying. Saunders gave herself over to the wonder of it, to the way Ford's lips moulded to her own, to the touch of his fingers on her cheek, her throat, to the touch of her own fingers in the crisp hair at his nape.

None of which, she thought a moment later, was any excuse for not hearing the approaching logging truck until it was sweeping past them in a cloud of dust, shaking the old Land Rover with the thunder of its passage, and saluting their kiss with a long, sneering blast of its air-horn!

'There, you see?' cried Ford as she reared back in surprise, breaking free of his arms. 'All I have to do is kiss you and an audience is provided, but I'm damned if you can accuse me of it being *my* fault.'

'Well, it certainly wasn't mine,' she retorted, but it was too late, already the laughter was building in his black eyes, and it was, like the intimacy of his kisses, so totally contagious that she couldn't ignore it, couldn't maintain her anger even if she'd wanted to.

'Well, whose fault was it, then?' he demanded, that generous, mobile mouth already curving into the start of his laughter.

Laughter she could only share when each of them pointed at the other and cried, simultaneously, without having planned it, 'Yours!'

They were still chuckling a few minutes later when Ford slowed for the tiny old tin-mining community of Royal George, pointing to where a small river flowed almost through the backyards of the town.

'You get the occasional beryl crystal just there,' he said, 'and there's topaz and rock crystal in the river gravels too. From here north, right to the coast, is a paradise if you happen to be serious about fossicking.'

'Which I gather you are?'

'Lord, no! For me it's just a minor hobby, a logical offshoot of my profession, that's all. If I was serious about it, I'd be up a creek somewhere, up to my knees in icy water, with a gold-pan or a gem-sieve in my hands. *And* I'd have been there since dawn or before, let me tell you. A really serious fossicker wouldn't be caught dead taking the time to kiss a pretty girl on a country road in a place like this and in weather like this. Maybe in a howling blizzard, or something, but otherwise. . .'

He shook his head in mock dismay, sharing Saunders' grin.

'No, I am but a poor amateur, with far different priorities, although I have every intention before the day's out of showing you a bit of what fossicking is all about. I think you might enjoy it, provided *you* don't start taking it too seriously.'

'There isn't much danger of that,' she replied. 'But, speaking of day, are we really going to have time for all this? I mean, it's well into the afternoon already, and we're——'

'Not as far from Launceston as you'd expect,' he replied casually, not looking at her. 'We've been travelling in a big circle, actually.'

'Which doesn't escape the fact that it's getting a bit

late,' Saunders replied, a tiny, ever-so-faint frisson of something—suspicion—nibbling at her mind, then sliding away before she could truly identify it.

'You worry too much,' he replied calmly, but still not looking at her. 'We'll *make* time, if we have to. After all, there's nobody going to have cat-fits if we're not home in time for tea. Is there?'

Definitely suspicion, she realised. And made the conscious decision just to accept. . .for the moment.

They reached the small settlement of Avoca, where Ford turned right and brought his old vehicle up to cruising speed for the brief run to Fingal. Then he turned north again, into a maze of roads that decreased in quality the further they rolled and then lurched along.

As did the conversation. Ford now dominated it, rambling on at length about the mining history of the region in a monologue studded with words Saunders couldn't understand, but most of which ended it 'ite'. Apatite, granodiorite, cassiterite, pegmatite. . . The list went on and on and on.

Saunders hung on for dear life as the ancient vehicle scrambled down a rutted, rock-strewn track, thundered through a tiny dry creek-bed and laboured up the other side to where a steel barrier seemed to preclude further access. Not so. Ford leapt out with a ring of keys in his hand and within moments they were continuing, with the barrier locked again behind them. A second barrier, ten minutes further on, guarded a pass that had obviously been blasted through a solid wall of rock.

'Close your eyes,' he said, once that barrier, too, had been locked behind them and he was again in the driver's seat. 'But hang on, because from here it gets a bit rough.'

Saunders shuddered to think about that, compared to what they had already negotiated, but did as she was told. The truck bucked and lurched and growled, and spewed stones out behind as it slewed through a series of up-and-down curves, then mercifully came to a halt.

'Can I look now?' she asked, and added to herself, Do I want to?

'No, wait.'

She felt him descend from the vehicle, and a moment later her door opened and he took her arm to guide her down to a footing on solid ground, then walked her a few paces and turned her just so.

'Now,' he said, and Saunders was struck by something quite unique in his voice, something she couldn't recognise exactly. And another sound which was definitely familiar!

She opened her eyes, gasped with disbelief and closed them again immediately. But when she looked again nothing had changed; she was standing on the edge of a small rivulet, facing a miniature waterfall that splashed happily into a miniature pool of crystal water that lapped across gravel of almost rainbow hues.

It was like something from a postcard; squatting beside the pool was a miniature—or so it appeared—cabin, built entirely of stone, with a roof that was covered in. . .grass?

'Sod,' he replied matter-of-factly to her whispered question. 'A lot of work, but definitely in keeping, I've always thought.'

'It's beautiful, truly beautiful.'

'You might change that to "primitive" when you see the inside,' he replied, taking her by the hand and moving towards the small stone cabin.

'It's beautiful,' she insisted, closing her fingers into his and shoving her earlier suspicions to the back of her mind.

The inside of the cabin was like her first impression of the outside—neat, tidy, almost elfin. And strangely beautiful. There was a stone fireplace which took up all of one wall, a post-and-rail bed that was admittedly crude but somehow also in keeping, a table and some stools—obviously hand-made—and, most amazing of all, a stone sink with water piped from somewhere outside.

'You did all this, didn't you?'

She didn't really need to ask; she knew before the words were uttered. Ford might as well have signed his name to the place, as if it were a rare painting.

'I certainly wasn't the first one here,' he replied. 'It's been mined for gold, and tin, and I suspect the Aborigines might have camped here long before that; I've found what appear to be artefacts, anyway. Although not many.'

He smiled down at her, obviously pleased by her reaction to the place.

'Now, what about some coffee? And then I'll get you started on the fossicking part of this expedition. You go and have a wander around and I'll fix things up for smoko.'

He waved vaguely off to the left, where a grove of wattles shaded the rear of the cabin. 'There's a dunny back there if you need it—or a sort of one, anyway.'

Saunders went off to inspect the waterfall, returned about ten minutes later to his call, and found the coffee made and the small table laden with a variety of foodstuffs. It also appeared that he had unloaded virtually everything else from the vehicle; one corner of the small cabin was heaped with a variety of gear.

'I had to get at the toolbox,' he explained, without being asked. 'The old girl was making some very strange noises just as we arrived, and I thought I'd have a stickybeak while you're off seeking your fortune.'

He poured the coffee and they sat cornerwise to each other, sipping at it in silence, looking at each other, looking away again.

Saunders fancied she could *feel* the change in the atmosphere between them, could almost *see* the question growing into something tangible, alive in the room with them.

'Will you be able to fix the truck in time?'

There, she thought. It was out now. No longer slinking round the back of her mind, confusing things.

'I don't know,' he said. 'But if it's what I think it is, yes, and even if I can't fix it, it won't stop us from getting out in time to fly home. If that's what you want.'

He sipped again at his coffee, looking abstractedly into the fireplace at the neat structures of twigs and branches, all laid, just waiting for the match. Then he sighed and turned to face her again.

'It isn't just my peculiar version of the old running-out-of-petrol trick, if that's what you're thinking, Saunders. I'm a bit old for that one, don't you reckon?'

He looked away again, but didn't give her time to answer before he went on.

'I will admit, for what it's worth, that I did have visions of maybe persuading you to stay over, to make a weekend of it. But I had no intention of tricking you into it.'

Now Saunders could only stare down into her own coffee-cup. No sense in replying to his earlier question, which wasn't relevant and never had been. And she wasn't ready, for reasons she couldn't even describe to herself, to answer the unspoken question about whether she could be convinced to stay. She wasn't even that certain it had been a question. 'I did have visions', he'd said; had something happened to change his mind?

'I certainly wasn't accusing you of anything like that,' she finally managed to say, but deep in her heart she felt that she'd waited too long to say it. But she hadn't accused him, hadn't even thought of such a thing.

Ford didn't reply. He didn't look at her either, just sat sipping at his coffee and staring into the fireplace.

The atmosphere, she fancied, was becoming decidedly chilly, and her own mental state was contributing more to that than she wanted to face up to just this minute. Only one thing to do. . .

'Well, if time's of the essence, we'd best get a move on,' she said, draining the cup and rising quickly to her feet. 'Because I am *not* leaving until I've had the chance to try fossicking, as you promised me, and that's that!'

The look Ford shot her at that defied definition, but a few minutes later she was a hundred metres downstream from the cabin, a shovel in one hand and a gem-sieve in the other, her eyes flicking from the old gravel run he'd pointed out to his departing figure.

'An hour—no more,' he'd said, after showing her what to do and how to do it. Saunders looked down at her feet, swimming in the gumboots he'd lent her, and wondered how he could have walked away without laughing. Walking in the oversized boots made her as clumsy as a duck, but it wasn't that which bothered her. Even as she laboriously pushed the shovel into the gravel she was wondering what she'd done to make him change his mind about wanting her to stay.

'It was part of his plan all along,' she muttered to herself as she lifted a shovelful of material into the top sieve and knelt to manoeuvre the whole apparatus into the water. 'Damn the man anyway! All he had to do was *ask*; now he's convinced that I'm certain the whole exercise was underhanded or. . .or something!'

She continued her monologue as she washed the gravel in the top sieve, discarded the remains because nothing looked at all interesting, and began doing the same with what had filtered through to the finer mesh of the bottom sieve.

'I *didn't* accuse him,' she said to the fistfuls of stones she inspected and discarded. 'Not of anything.'

More gravel, more sluicing, more careful inspection of the remains. Within minutes she had established a comfortable rhythm, even if the whole process seemed fruitless. In half an hour she found a couple of pieces of what she thought were petrified wood and half a dozen other bits that were interesting enough to set aside for Ford's expert evaluation.

But she was no clearer in her mind, which she was beginning to think would benefit from a trip through the gem-sieves. Ford had hoped she might prove amenable to being persuaded to stay the weekend, he'd said. No mention of where they might stay, or in what circumstances, although it wasn't difficult to assume he'd had this place in mind.

'It isn't as if there was a written contract saying you absolutely *must* sleep with him as part of the deal, you know' she told herself.

Except that she wanted to; that was half—no, almost all—the problem. She did, and Ford Landell knew that she did, and she knew that he knew. . .

'And you, you silly goose, knew damned well when you accepted the invitation that it might come to this,' she continued aloud. 'You *hoped* it would, even if you didn't know then what you'd do about it when the time came. And now the time has come and you *still* don't know.'

But she did. She knew that she wanted Ford; she knew that he wanted her. And she knew—no doubt about it—that with this type of man, this man especially, she would always have the choice; Ford Landell would never force himself upon her or any other woman.

Neither was he a trophy-hunter; Simon had said that and she had believed him, had known it herself, instinctively. No, the problem was not, she admitted, Ford Landell at all. The problem was herself.

'What are you waiting for—a marriage proposal, complete with ring?'

The bitterness in her own voice surprised her, and she looked up, half expecting somehow to find it was someone else who'd spoken, then shook her head in silent mockery of herself.

Then a movement caught her eye, something swimming in the next pool downstream. A fish? As she watched there was a dark shape, that surfaced and then dived again, but it was no shape she could recognize, identify.

Slipping out of the cumbersome boots, she moved

up on to the bank and began to stalk her way downstream, carefully taking each step as she picked her way barefoot over the gravel banks. The animal—she was now certain that it was no fish—surfaced again, but still she was too far away to get a proper look.

The left-handed bank—her side—climbed upward, forming the outer curve around the edge of the pool. If she could reach the crest she would be able to look down, have a clear view. . .

Saunders crept closer, then flopped down on her belly and crawled the last few metres to where she would peer down into the crystal waters of the pool. So clear was the water that she might have been *in* it; within moments she discerned the flashing movement of two small fish as they slid magically through the water beneath her.

On the other side of the pool a small trout leapt clear of the water, after some insect or another, she supposed, and then, right beneath her, a sleek brown form moved into view, nuzzling into the gravel bottom with its unmistakable, bill-like snout.

Saunders lay there, transfixed. She was a city girl, and although of course, she knew about platypuses, she had never seen one alive—much less in the wild. And, from this vantage-point, every detail of the astonishing animal was as clear as if she'd been swimming beside it: the beaver tail, the bill like a duck, the webbed feet with their enormous claws. . .

Saunders? Saunders. . .where have you got to?'

The voice carried on the breeze, only just loud enough to be a whisper when it reached her, hardly louder than the audible crunch of Ford's boots on the gravel. She rolled to her knees and saw him approaching, lifted her arm to wave him towards her, lifted her finger to her lips in a silent bid for quiet, then rolled back to peer down again at the rare animal below her.

'Are you all right?' Ford asked in a whisper as he loomed up behind her, his eyes intent not on the water, she noticed, but on her, his eyes worried, filled with concern.

'Of course I am,' she whispered back. 'But look. . . Just look. . .'

Ford's smile was warm, gentle, indulgent; this was nothing new for him, this sighting of a platypus. He knelt, then sprawled out beside Saunders and silently joined her vigil.

They lay there, shoulder to shoulder, flank to flank, and she gradually became aware of the heat from his body as they both concentrated on watching the monotreme. But her awareness of him was only secondary, overshadowed by her fascination with the platypus, until he spoke.

'We have to get moving soon; the truck's OK, after all, but we've run out of time, I'm afraid.'

Saunders kept her eyes on the furry body of the platypus, but her mind had left it now. Still, she didn't dare turn to look at Ford, knew that if she did she would never manage to say what she wanted to say. She shifted only enough to be able to point down at the water.

'Will he be here tomorrow?'

'I'd expect so; he lives here,' Ford replied, after what seemed a very long time. And then, after an even longer time, 'But why?'

He was looking at her now; she could sense it. But Saunders was stricken with an insane shyness, and couldn't meet his eyes.

'I'd like to see him again,' she finally managed to

whisper, forcing out the words, knowing she sounded melodramatic, but unable to help that.

This time the silence between them was sheer torture, and her mind raced in a noisy silence of its own. Had she insulted him somehow? Did he really want her to stay, or had she entirely misinterpreted everything?

You ninny, she thought angrily. Why can't you just out and *say* that you want to stay? And if that means sleeping with the man, well, damn it—say that too! Because it's what you want, and he already knows that better than you do.

She could still feel Ford's eyes on her, and now she could also feel the tension growing between them where their shoulders and hips were linked by tongues of fire. She closed her eyes, opened them, closed them again, but couldn't quite force herself to glace sideways, much less turn that extra little bit to face him directly.

Say something, damn it, she thought. But when he did, it was in a voice so soft she could barely hear. But it was loud enough to dissolve the tension instantly.

'Just because he lives here it doesn't guarantee we'll see him, Saunders.'

'Just because there are gemstones here it doesn't mean I'll find any,' she replied. 'But I still want to try.'

'You'll find them,' he said. 'Probably easier than I'll manage to catch us a trout or two for dinner.' And he rolled away from her and came to his feet in a single, flowing movement.

Then she had to look at him, if only so she could reach up and grasp the hand he extended to her. There he was: Fordon Landell. Same silvery hair, same laughing black eyes, no horns and tail, no sudden transformation to demon or devil. Safe, she thought. But wondered as they walked back to the cabin how long that safeness would last. . .and how long she really wanted it to.

CHAPTER ELEVEN

FORD had lied about the fishing. Or got lucky. Saunders wasn't able to determine which; she could only observe how easy he made it look, how smoothly he could deposit a trout-fly in what—to her—seemed to be just the right place at just the right time to have a fish come from nowhere to offer itself as a culinary sacrifice.

He only had to make half a dozen casts near the head of the platypus pool before he caught the first fish, and she was entranced by the performance, by the fish leaping into the air and fighting for its freedom. Not so entranced when Ford dipped his hand into the water, caught up the small trout, laughed at it, said something she didn't hear, and released it.

'Too small,' he mouthed at her. Then, louder, 'Just a baby; we'll have a try now and see if his daddy is there.'

Saunders nodded an acceptance, then settled back on her haunches to watch him, marvelling at the rhythm and grace with which he manipulated the fly-rod. Back and forth and back and forth, with all the flair of those girls who did baton work with ribbons, and then, with no specific impetus she could see, he would reach out just that little bit further to deposit the fly, as light as thistledown, then watch as it drifted down through the pool.

Ford moved through the edges of the pool in bare feet, the water lapping sometimes to his knees, some-

times to the edges of his brief shorts. He seemed
impervious to the coldness of the water, so totally
engrossed was he in the pursuit, in the hunt.

'Hah! You're a bit more like it.'

And so it must have been. This fish didn't leap; it
surged in a swirl on the surface, then sped off down
the pool, bending the fishing-rod into a tight bow as
Ford laughed with delight.

'Oh, you beauty,' he said, then shouted to Saunders
without taking his eyes from the swiftly moving fish.
'I've been after this one for five years, now. He's a
ripper fish—feed us for a week if I can land him.'

Then he lapsed into silence, clearly transfixed by his
battle with the fish as it surged through the pool,
tearing line from Ford's reel and showing no sign of
easy capitulation.

Saunders was on her feet now, dancing with excitement as Ford surged down the edge of the pool,
moving deeper and deeper into the water as he followed the fish, laughing wildly and shouting encouragement all the way.

'Go, you beauty! Go! Oh, you little ripper!'

He was more than waist-deep now, and in a moment
even deeper, the water up to his chest as he struggled
to keep up with the fish that was steadily moving down
the pool and showing no sign of tiring.

The great fish leapt, but only once. Which was
enough, at least, for Saunders to see how big it really
was, how truly magnificent in its battle for freedom.
Then it was surging down the pool again, moving
around in a broad circle as it moved towards some
destination only it could know.

Ford shouted encouragement, and Saunders suddenly realised that she, too, was doing that—encouragement for the fish, not the fisherman.

But too late; the fish hadn't quite made it to the shelter it sought, and she found herself watching with a growing sensation of concern as Ford began to make up line, to bring the great fish in closer and closer to where he stood—thigh-deep now—in the water.

The rod bowed, the line angled so close that he could run his fingers down it, and then, suddenly, there was an almighty flurry of man and fish, and water flashing in the evening sunlight, and the fish was gone.

Ford moved as if exhausted, wading his way to the shore. But his eyes were alive, his smile so radiant it rivalled the dying sun.

'Wonderful!' he cried as he reached the shore. 'Wasn't he brilliant? That's the fourth time I've had him on, and this time I very nearly *did* have him!'

It wasn't until he'd reached the gravel bank where Saunders waited that he quieted, sobered.

'Not that it does us much good for tea; I hope you don't mind too much,' he said. 'We'll have a check on the pool below the waterfall; there's usually a couple of good fish there too.'

Saunders didn't reply. She walked with him up to the waterfall pool, even waded in herself to grab up the second of the two trout he caught there, but she didn't dare to discuss *the* fish. Not here, not now.

He had *let* the great fish escape; she was sure of it without knowing exactly why. Although she knew nothing about fishing, had no real evidence to support her feeling.

And, once they had returned to the stone cabin, she found herself with other, more immediate concerns than an escaped fish of whatever size. The small cabin, which at first impression had seemed merely pictur-esque, took on an entire new dimension now that she was inside it with Ford Landell and committed to spending the night there with him.

When they had arrived the cabin had been seemingly dominated by the fireplace which comprised one entire wall. But now, entering the building behind Ford Landell, it seemed to Saunders that what dominated the room was the bed!

Hand-made, a simple enough apparatus of post-and-rail framing with a tight-woven base of what appeared to be nylon rope, it was the only place for Saunders to sit while Ford began to lay out the cooking utensils and other gear he'd brought in from the vehicle. He had already laden the stools in the room with boxes, and the table-top was also covered.

The bed squealed when Saunders perched gingerly on the edge of it, never taking her eyes from the tall, muscular figure that moved confidently through the confines of the tiny building. And suddenly she was too aware of the still moist shorts that clung to his hips, of the long, strong, length of leg, the fact that in the damp clothing he could almost as well have worn nothing at all.

Every time she shifted her weight the bed shrieked; every time that happened Ford would pause and look at her, a faint, half-amused smile growing on his mobile lips.

He didn't talk to her, and she didn't—couldn't—think of anything to say, wasn't sure she dared. The decision to stay the night had been made; she was committed now. But night was a long way off; it was still barely twilight outside, and already the waiting was starting to push her nerves.

She ought to be helping, she thought. But there wasn't room! Being in the cabin with Ford was like trying to share the cooking in a kitchen designed for one. Saunders shifted again, the bed squeaked again, Ford looked at her again and smiled again. Then he went on unpacking—a gas lantern, a cooler loaded with. . .something, various plates and dishes and cutlery. All to be laid out in some preconceived plan that only Ford knew.

'Be a while until tea. Would you like another coffee?'

His voice seemed to echo through the cabin, emphasising its isolation, its smallness.

'Have you room to make it?'

That brought a smile; Saunders could feel the atmosphere softening because of it.

'I'll make room. Have to anyway, if we're going to have any place to sleep.'

Sleep. Just that word caused a frisson of sensation inside her, a shiver she desperately hoped he couldn't see. But he didn't need to see; he knew exactly what she was feeling, Saunders thought. Better, perhaps, than she did herself.

How many women, she wondered, had shared this cabin with Ford Landell? She looked at the narrowness of the bed she was perched on, and fought against the mental images of bodies entwined on it—*his* body, warm and throbbing, against that of. . .

'I never noticed before how small this place is,' he was saying then. 'Mind you, I hadn't really been planning for company when I built it, and this is the first time anybody's ever stayed over with me.'

Damn him, she thought. He was reading her mind again, or else was so finely tuned to her responses that he appeared able to read her mind. Either choice was disconcerting, worrying.

'D'you suppose you could have a go at blowing this thing up while you're sitting there?' he asked, handing her a limp, deflated air-mattress.

'Of course,' Saunders replied, at first glad of being able just to do *something*, anything but sit there like a lump. Then she caught Ford's glimmer of a smile as he handed it to her, and noticed the slightly raised eyebrow, the devilish look in those dark eyes.

Like a prisoner being asked to dig his own grave, she thought, and shuddered inwardly as the phrase recurred over and over in her mind with each exhalation as she began to blow up the air-mattress.

She was only halfway through when he stopped her by tapping her on the shoulder. She looked up to find him holding out a coffee-cup while gesturing with his free hand for her to hand him the partially inflated mattress.

'You'll end up hyperventilating if you keep at it like that,' he said. 'There's plenty of time, you know. It isn't even gone dark yet.'

So why, having taken it from her with fingers that seemed to burn her own with that single, slight touch as they made the exchange, did he stand there and finish inflating the mattress with just a few massive breaths? The air-mattress hung between them, swelling visibly as he breathed into it, then he gestured her to rise, and, after ramming the plug home with the heel of his hand, he laid the mattress down and nodded for her to sit again.

Saunders held the cup in both hands, fearful even then that her trembling fingers might cause the contents to slop over, even more fearful that Ford would notice her nervousness to the point where he might have to let her *know* that he was noticing.

Again she found herself perched on the edge of the bed, suddenly aware of the side-rail as it dug into her thighs, more aware of how Ford looked at her, of the speculative, enigmatic look in his eyes, of how those eyes roamed over her face, her body. Possessively, knowingly.

This time when she shivered, it was visible to both of them.

'You're cold,' he said, as if only just aware of it. He strode over to the heap of gear from the truck, hefted out her suitcase and brought it to her. 'You don't want to let yourself get a chill, Saunders,' he said. 'And it's easy done, here; the warmth goes quickly with the sun.'

He stood there for a moment, causing Saunders to wonder if he expected her to get changed there and then, with him providing an audience, then suddenly turned and slipped through the door, picking up his own kit-bag as he did so.

'I'll change too, I think,' he said on the way out. 'And I'll just grab a wash and a bit of wood while I'm at it, so you won't have to rush.'

But she did rush. Saunders threw open her suitcase and quickly yanked out a pair of jeans and a bulky, oversized jumper. She paused only long enough to peer out of the window and spot Ford sauntering down towards the waterfall, then she threw off her skimpy shorts and the tank-top and pulled on the more substantial clothing. She was breathing quickly, almost panting as she thought for an instant, then pulled the sweater back off so she could put on a T-shirt under it, cinched a belt through the loops in the jeans, pulled on heavy socks and her walking-boots, laced right to the tops and firmly knotted. Like a suit of armour, she thought wildly, wishing she had something similar to protect her mind.

And then she paced. Four steps to the creaky, deceptively innocent bed, five steps to the window, where, in an aberrant shaft of the dying sun, she could see Ford Landell standing naked beneath the waterfall, both hands raised as he rinsed his silvery hair, the water streaming down his arms, his muscular chest, through the darker hair, the shadowy area of his loins. The scene lasted only for an instant before the light was changed by a passing cloud, but it stayed in her mind as if etched there.

He returned some time later, his silvery hair slicked down and wet, his body lithe and trim in jeans and a bulky woodsman's shirt, his arms filled with wood for the fireplace and his eyes filled with. . .something. But just exactly what it was, Saunders couldn't decide and didn't even think to enquire. Not out loud.

But as he started the actual preparations for dinner, firing up the camping stove, heating just a small amount of oil in it, slicing potatoes into thin slices, he kept looking at her. And his eyes inevitably, on those occasions that she dared meet them, danced with laughter. It seemed almost as if he expected her to understand the joke, whatever it was, to laugh with him.

Saunders just fidgeted. She could do nothing else; there was no room for her to help, hardly room for her even to move. She could only sit on the edge of that *damned* bed, her nervous fingers plucking at the edges of the air-mattress, her ears tuned to the squeak of the bed every time she moved, her eyes locked on Ford's every movement.

She watched the deft movements of his fingers, the way he would occasionally sweep back an errant lock of hair from his forehead, the look of concentration he got when peeling and slicing the potatoes, the way his jeans fitted snugly over muscular legs, the taut, slender, masculine hips. And he was aware of her scrutiny; he couldn't help but be aware, she thought. Eventually, however, he proved it.

'Saunders,' he said, after the umpteenth squeak of the traitorous bed, speaking without even bothering to look over at her, 'I don't know what's got you so frothy, but I don't think this cabin is big enough for the both of us, at least when I'm trying to create a culinary masterpiece. Why don't you go for a walk—look at the sunset, or something? I'll call you for tea when it's ready.'

She leaped at the chance, was halfway out of the door almost before he'd finished speaking. He had to halt her with a word so that he could add, 'And I'm quite capable of cooking this repast, you know. So you can stop being so nervous about it all. I won't burn the fish or set the place on fire or. . .whatever.'

All of which would have been quite reassuring if she hadn't caught that gleam of laughter in his eyes, hadn't seen the way he ran his eyes over her from crown to bootlaces—about as subtle as a cannibal chef.

None the less, stepping out into the dying daylight was, she thought, what it must feel like to be released from gaol. The tense silence of the interior gave way immediately to the sounds of birds, the touch of the breeze along her cheeks. She no longer felt the intensity of being always within touching distance of the man she wanted to touch, the man she wanted to touch her, but didn't dare to make the first move towards.

She wandered down to sit on a driftwood log, staring into the prisms of the sunset light through the mist created by the waterfall. Ford, she was becoming increasingly certain, was playing some game with her, perhaps with both of them. And the more she thought about it, the more confusing it became, the more frustrating.

She had made it quite clear that she wanted to stay the night with him, but had she not made it clear enough that she knew what it would entail, that she wanted that too? Or was he being the obtuse one, and doing it deliberately?

'What does he want—for me to throw myself at him?' she muttered, picking up yet another pebble to chuck into the pond so she could watch the ripples. Then she looked again at the falling water, and her mind superimposed that earlier view of Ford standing naked there. Saunders shivered, but it wasn't because she was cold.

She looked back at the cabin, made a quick mental calculation of the time she would need, then peeled off her clothing even more quickly than she'd put it on. Damn Ford anyway, she thought, and that thought sustained her as she marched into the chilly water and stood beneath the waterfall, feeling the icy streams as they flooded her hair, sluiced down across her shoulders, her breasts, her fluttering tummy, her trembling legs. After a minute, the water seemed to get less cold, but never really warm. After that initial instant of shock, she found it possible to reach down for handfuls of fine sand to wash with, almost came to enjoy the experience, actually.

She never once took her eyes from the dark shape of the cabin window, never once saw even the slightest movement, the slightest indication that Ford might be watching her as she had watched him. But he was; somehow she knew it, and was glad of it.

By the time he emerged to call out to her, Saunders had used the T-shirt to dry herself, had put the rest of her clothing back on, and was sitting innocently watching the water. It was no great task to hang the damp T-shirt on the bumper-bar of the vehicle as she passed it, but holding her nerve as she entered the cabin wasn't quite so easy.

Especially when she found, after blinking once or twice to adjust her eyes to the unexpectedly dim light, that Ford had been busy—*very* busy—during her absence. The small table was tidily laid for two, with a table-cloth, no less! The lantern hung, waiting to be lit if needed, but the table held a candle, already flickering its small store of light in competition with the bustling fire in the huge fireplace, and a bottle of wine, even.

But it was the bed which caught her eye, now spread with a sleeping-bag, even a pillow—with a sprig of bright yellow blossoms decorating it.

Ford turned from the camp stove and offered a hand, leading Saunders to her seat and then bowing with exaggerated flair.

'My apologies about the quality of the crystal,' he said with a smile, indicating the two tin cups from which they had drunk at lunchtime, 'but on these rough roads, you understand. . .'

He poured a tiny bit of wine, a cloth over one arm, and with all the officiousness of the snootiest wine steward, nodding at the appropriate times as Saunders, falling into her own role, sniffed the offering, sipped at it, and signalled her approval.

'An excellent choice, madam,' he said as he poured each of them a 'glass'. 'Definitely from steep, stony ground, perhaps a bit long in the tooth, but with short legs and fat ankles, I venture.'

Saunders chuckled, then found herself relaxing as Ford turned away and began to serve the meal. First a clear, rich, consommé, delicately flavoured with herbs. Then the fish, perfectly sautéed and accompanied by wafer-thin fried potatoes. For dessert, he had peeled and sectioned several mandarin oranges and arranged them artfully in a plastic bowl.

And, of course, there was the wine, which made it all the more easy for Saunders to slip into the artificial mood so carefully created for her. The meal was superb, the conversation light, polite, non-threatening and thoroughly enjoyable. By the time they had finished it all the daylight had fled and the fireplace was down to gently glowing coals; only the flickering of the candle provided any light at all.

It was just right for the mood he'd created, but somehow not quite enough to sustain the conversation. It cast subtle shadows in the small cabin, and each time Saunders looked at her companion the light seemed to cast his face in a different mould. At one glance it softened his features, giving her the impression of what he must have looked like as a much younger man. But at the next it put a diabolical cast to his countenance, emphasising the strong bones, the harsh planes of his face as it now was.

And always the flickering light changed his eyes, those dark, dark eyes, veiled by lashes any woman would envy, that now seemed to watch her with some secret knowledge behind them, a sort of brooding, a kind of speculation, too much silence.

Saunders felt her nervousness returning with a rush, but it was different now, somehow less threatened. She was simply much more aware of the man who sat, totally at ease, catty-corner from her and actually only inches away. Silent, looking at her, waiting. . .

The candle guttered; the silence deepened. Saunders felt as if all the air had departed the room, knew that if she didn't speak, or move, or. . .something, she would disintegrate, fly into a million separate pieces. What she said was the first thing that came to mind.

'You let that big fish go, didn't you?'

'I'm surprised you noticed, but yes.'

'Why?'

Her voice was soft, almost a whisper against the silence. His was equally soft, but not really a whisper. Just. . .soft.

'Timing,' he said. Then the silence thundered down again.

'I don't understand,' Saunders said.

A minute later? An hour? Long enough, anyway, for his hand to reach across the corner of the table, to pick up another hand, turn it over in his long fingers. She could only watch with disembodied, casual interest.

'It wasn't the right time. That's all.'

'But. . .but you said you had been trying for. . .for years,' she protested, confused more than ever, and yet maybe not so confused after all.

'And I might be trying for years yet,' he said. 'If I'd taken him today, I wouldn't be able to do that, would I?'

'You're saying it's the thrill of the chase, not the

capture that's so important?' she rejoined, wondering as she spoke how, if that theory were applied, it applied to her. Was he only chasing her because of the challenge?'

'Timing,' he said then, in a voice barely audible. 'Timing is everything.'

'You've lost me again,' Saunders said. Now she was becoming increasingly aware of how his fingers were manipulating her own, caressing, stroking, but with an abstract quality to the process; her fingers, she thought, might as easily have been worry beads.

Ford sighed, fell silent, stayed silent for long moments before he tried again to explain.

'Timing,' he said, shrugging his shoulders, looking at Saunders with eyes now alive with expression. 'Today, I didn't set out to catch that fish. I had. . . other things in mind, other priorities. Catching him was a matter of luck, an accident, not because I was devoting myself to the situation. I guess what I'm saying is that the fish deserved better than that.'

'But you were fishing! You were out there specifically to catch a fish.'

His laugh was glowing, mellow, gentle. And now his fingers were at her wrist, stroking her pulse, lifting it, setting it afire.

'The fish I was setting out to catch were only minnows,' he said. 'Bait. I had much bigger game in mind and you know it, Saunders. It was *you* I wanted to catch.'

'A game,' she said. 'Is that all there is to it—just a game?' She waved in a vague gesture over the table. 'Is that all this is—just bait?'

'You know better than that.'

'I only wish I did.' The tried vaguely to free her

hand, but it wasn't much of a try. His fingers continued
their manipulation of her pulse.

'But you do. You just don't want to admit it to
yourself, that's all.'

'Admit what?' Stupid question—she *knew*, and he
knew she knew. Which was why he didn't answer, she
supposed, only smiled at her with his mouth and
laughed at her with his eyes.

'You have to stop,' she finally said. 'You can't just
keep on doing this to me.'

'Doing what? Wanting you? Loving you? Teasing?
Of course I can. And I will, too, especially the teasing.'
He wasn't questioning now, but musing. Still holding
her with his eyes, with his fingers. 'Yes,' he finally
continued, 'I guess you'd know about teasing,
Saunders. . . But there under that waterfall, driving
me crazy deliberately. You're lucky you got fed; I
came *that* close to letting the tucker just burn so that I
could come and join you. I should have, really.'

Somehow, without her noticing, he had lifted her
wrist; now he moved his mouth to it, and his lips were
brands, searing against her pulse, boiling her blood.
And somehow he had left his chair, had drawn her
upright from her own chair, his other arm round her
waist, his strength countering the fact that her legs
were like rubber, melting from the fire in her belly, in
her loins.

'Yes, you should have,' she managed to whisper,
before his mouth swooped down to stop her, before
his arms closed round her to pull her against the
warmth of him, against the warmth and the strength
and the rising tide of lust that met her own.

Then there was only a kaleidoscope of sensation,
scattered, fleeing impressions, of clothing coming off

to land where it fell, of Ford's lips as they sipped at her nipples, drawing them to roseate peaks of exquisite tenderness, of his fingers tracing lines of fire along her thighs, her tummy, lines that his lips could follow, and did, as they roamed inexorably to the core of her womanhood.

Somehow the air mattress was lifted from the creaking bed, somehow the fire—at some point in the proceedings—was replenished with fuel, so that it could cast a flickering, warming glow over lovemaking that needed no external warmth, that certainly had sufficient fuel of its own.

Saunders found her skin uniquely sensitised; a touch anywhere from his lips, his wondrous fingers—sent spasms of delight through her like ripples in the platypus pond, sometimes raising moans of pleasure, sometimes forcing uncontainable laughter to burst from her swollen lips.

Again and again he brought her to the edge of fulfilment, only to stall there with knowing, frustrating, delightful expertise, attuned to her needs as if she were a fine, delicate living musical instrument. . .or an orchestra set to play the whole night long.

Beside them the fire calmed to gentle coals, but her own fires and his seemed inexhaustible, never quite calming, just leaping from fever-pitch to furnace-heat with the simplest touch of lip or tongue or teasing finger.

When finally Ford allowed her to plunge over the crest of the wave of passion he had forged, it was only to plunge after her, then to lift her gently, speedily, inexorably upward again. And when they were finally spent there was the sleeping-bag to cover them, the warmth of their bodies to cling to. . .

* * *

'Are you going to sleep forever? It's time to get up.'

The voice was a whisper in her ear, accompanied by tantalising touches of his fingers along her waist, her hip, her thigh. Saunders wriggled closer, revelling in his touch, in the warmth of him against her.

His slow moan of pleasure was shattered by the maniacal laugh of a kookaburra somewhere outside, and she chuckled. 'Ah, the timing,' she sighed. 'We're back to having an audience again, I see.'

'That doesn't answer my question,' he replied. 'And it isn't half as funny as that damned bird thinks it is.'

Then his lips were moving across her own, touching briefly as they roamed down her cheek, following a recent trail along her shoulder, then down to where they could graze at her breast.

Saunders ran her own lips down the line of his neck, smelling the clean scent of his hair, feeling its coarse texture against her cheek. There was no sense of urgency now in their lovemaking; that had gone with the wild freedom of the night. Now his touch, and hers too, was languid, tantalising, teasing.

'Why *should* I get up?' she asked. 'I suppose you expect me to get the fire going, put the coffee on, cook breakfast?'

'I'm just a bit worried that if you don't get up, and soon, we might never manage it,' he replied from somewhere beneath the sleeping-bag. 'You expect an awful lot from a man with an empty stomach, Nurse White. Where's your professional compassion, anyway?'

'Just about. . .there,' she sighed.

And, many, many minutes later, chuckled again, as the kookaburra voiced his hysterical approval.

Then she squealed with surprise as Ford erupted

from the sleeping-bag, throwing her over his shoulder as he plunged through the door and charged naked towards the waterfall pool.

'I'll teach you to laugh at me,' he howled. 'Cold showers all round—that's *my* prescription, Nurse.

'Besides,' he said a few moments later, shivering just slightly as he laved Saunders' trembling body with the icy water, adding to the water's effect with strategic touches of his magic fingers, 'I've been wanting to do this since yesterday. Audience or no audience.' Then he grinned mischievously. 'No, since long before that, actually, I've sort of wanted to do this since the first time I saw you, if the truth be told.

'You're a sadist,' she replied. 'And, what's more, I doubt if you even remember the first time you saw me.'

'Of course I do. You were with that amazingly rude woman, the one who got all strange and abusive because I held the door open for her. You, I might add, were not impressed.'

'I was very impressed with you; I suppose it's safe to admit that now. I didn't think you'd even noticed me.'

'Oh, yes, you did; you went all flustered, as I recall, when I turned up at your office, I sometimes wonder if that's why you got so stroppy with me.'

'I didn't!'

'You certainly did,' he said, turning her with gentle hands so that he could look into her eyes. 'You were unimpressed—distinctly unimpressed—with my views on diabetes and heredity.' And then he laughed—hugely, delightedly. 'And if you'd known then that it was *you* I had in mind as the prospective mother. . .'

'I'd have thought you quite mad,' Saunders replied

rather primly, a difficult thing to do considering their situation and what he was doing with his hands.

'And I *did* think I was mad,' came the reply. 'But I feel much better about it now, since the discussion has become something more than theoretical; I'm quite prepared to bow to your superior wisdom on the subject. After that fabulous speech you wrote, with *us* in mind. . .' Then he frowned. 'That's assuming we're going to have children; we haven't really talked about that yet.'

'I did not write that speech for us,' Saunders insisted. Perhaps lying just a teeny bit, but safe enough, she thought, in that. 'Actually,' she teased, 'I must admit that I sort of had you and Nadine in mind.'

Ford laughed, the sound gurgling in her ear beside the rushing of the water around them.

'And you accuse *me* of fishing? Nadine, I will tell you now, and never mention her again, was quite simply never in the hunt. Nadine is a self-centred, selfish, immature, childish brat—and that's on her good days, of which there are few. I occasionally used to take her out in deference to her dear old daddy, who is a very good friend of mine and who worries—quite rightly, too!—about the company she keeps.'

'Ah,' said Saunders. 'Just good friends, eh?'

'Not good friends,' he replied hotly. 'More like being saddled with a precocious, spoiled nine-year-old most of the time. But her father helped me a good deal when I was starting out on my own, and I've always sort of felt I owed him something.'

He paused, leant down to kiss her, to pull her against the warm strength of him. 'Now, does that satisfy your curiosity? Or have you got a whole list of questions about the women in my wicked, wanton past?'

'I'm actually more interested in the future,' Saunders replied, moving her hands down his chest to flutter her fingers along the muscular ribbing of his torso, those amazingly narrow hips. 'Like, when are we going to get started on this fossicking business? You promised me gemstones, Ford Landell, not reminiscences from your murky past. And I intend to hold you to that.'

'So I noticed,' he replied, his voice quivering as he leant down to capture her lips, his hands moving round her body to pull her closer against him.

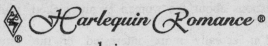

Harlequin Romance ®

brings you

SIMPLY THE BEST

Authors you'll treasure, books you'll want to keep!

Harlequin Romance books just keep getting better and better...and we're delighted to welcome you to our **Simply the Best** showcase for 1997, highlighting a special author each month!

Watch for:

#3448 GETTING OVER HARRY
by Renee Roszel

Emily has been jilted at the altar, and her best friend, Meg, convinces her to take a holiday to get over it. But Emily refuses to be persuaded that the best cure for a broken heart is another romance. Enter Lyon Gallant on the scene: he's rich, he's cute—and he wants Emily!

"Renee Roszel heats up your reading pleasure."
—*Romantic Times*

"Fast moving and entertaining, sparkling to the very end!" —*Affaire de Coeur* on *Dare to Kiss a Cowboy*

"Ms Roszel produces exciting characters and dialogue that packs a punch."
—*Rendezvous*

Available in March wherever
Harlequin books are sold.

Harlequin Romance ®

brings you

BABY BOOM

We are proud to announce the birth of our new bouncing baby series— Baby Boom!

Each month in 1997 we'll be bringing you your very own bundle of joy—a cute, delightful romance by one of your favorite authors. Our heroes and heroines are about to discover that two's company and three (or four...or five) is a family!

This exciting new series is all about the true labor of love...

Parenthood, and how to survive it!

Watch for:
#3450 HIS BROTHER'S CHILD
by Lucy Gordon

When Donna's fiancé, Toni, was cruelly snatched away from her, his brother, Rinaldo Mantini, insisted she marry *him!* He wouldn't allow her baby to be born out of wedlock. To marry Rinaldo was to marry her greatest enemy, but how could Donna deny him the chance to care for his brother's child?

Available in March wherever Harlequin books are sold.